Ketogen

The Ultimate Ketogenic Diet Guide For Beginners

(Learn How To Start The Ketogenic Diet The Right Way)

Rickey Patton

Table Of Contents

Salmon And Feta Burger

Looking forward to healthy life.

Ingredients:

- Pepper
- 3Tbsp. lemon juice
- 2 lb. salmon
- ghee
- 2 oz. crumbled feta cheese
- 2 spinach
- Sauce
- sour cream
- 2 minced garlic clove
- some lemon juice
- 2 avocado

Directions:

1. Take the skin from the salmon slice up.
2. Now place the pieces into your food processor along with the spinach and then process these until the spinach is

combined, but the mixture isn't too mushy.

3. This step is important.
4. Add this mixture into a bowl along with the pepper, lemon juice, ghee, and feta.
5. Mix to make it well combined.
6. Divide this mixture into 10 patties.
7. Then bring out a skillet and then add some oil.
8. Heat it up before cooking the patties for 5 to 10 minutes.
9. Please turn around and cook a bit longer.
10. While this is cooking, you can work on the sauce.
11. One thing remains to be done now. Mash the avocado until smooth and then throw in your other ingredients.
12. Finally spread this out over the burgers and then serve!

Wonderful Grilled Tomatoes
With Apricot Jam

Ingredients:

- 4tbsp. olive oil
- 12 medium tomatoes
- 6tsp. dried oregano
- Salt and pepper to taste
- 8oz. grated gouda cheese
- 4 oz. watercress
- 4tsp. sugarfree apricot jam

Directions:

1. Preheat oven to 370°F.
2. Lightly grease a baking tray and put tomatoes.
3. This step is important.
4. Spread some jam over tomato slices.
5. Sprinkle generous amount of dried oregano.
6. Add grated cheese on top, bake for 45 to 50 minutes, or until you see cheese turns to golden brown.
7. Finally add watercress, drizzle some olive oil, and add cracked black pepper.

Titanic Cauliflower Bake

Ingredients:

- 6 oz. cream cheese
- 1 cup heavy cream
- 12 slices bacon, cooked and crumbled
- 6 tablespoons butter
- 2 cup chopped green onionss
- Salt and pepper to taste
- 2 simply head cauliflower, cut into florets
- 4 cups sharp cheddar cheese, shredded and separated

Directions:

1. Preheat your oven to 390degrees F.
2. Boil some water in a fresh pot and then blanch the cauliflower florets for 5 to 10 minutes.
3. This step is important.
4. Once done, drain the water.

5. In another pot, add the butter, heavy cream, cream cheese, 3 cup of cheddar cheese, salt and pepper.
6. Mix well to combine.
7. Once the cheese and butter has melted, turn off the heat
8. Now In a baking dish, evenly add the cauliflower florets and the cheese sauce.
9. Then add the bacon and green onionss but make sure you reserve 2 tablespoon of each.
10. Stir the ingredients together.
11. Top with the rest of the cheddar cheese and the reserved green onionss and crumbled bacon.
12. One thing remains to be done now.
13. Bake for 40 to 45 minutes or until the cauliflower is soft and the cheese is bubbly.
14. Finally serve immediately.

Crock Pot Chicken Chowder

Looking forward to healthy life.

Ingredients:

- 30 oz. of diced tomatoes
- 2 medium diced onions
- 100 g lime juice
- 4 Tbsp. cilantro, chopped
- 2 clove of garlic, chopped
- 2 tsp. salt
- 30 g jalapeno, diced
- 2 lb. chicken breasts, boneless and skinless
- 16oz. of cream cheese
- 4Tbsp. black pepper
- 2 cup of chicken broth

Directions:

1. Combine all the ingredients into a crockpot.
2. One thing remains to be done now. Cook on high for 6hours or on low for 10 hours.

3. Finally when cooked shred the chicken in the crock pot using 6 forks and serve.

Quick Mushroom Crust Pizza

Ingredients:

- 8tablespoons olive oil
- 4 Portobello Mushroom Caps
- 6tablespoons fresh basil, minced Dash of salt
- 6ounces mozzarella cheese, cubed
- Dash of pepper
- 16slices pepperoni 2 medium tomato

Directions:

1. Scrape the gills and stems of the mushrooms out using a spoon and discard of them.
2. This step is important. By the end, your mushroom tops should be 4cm thick.
3. Preheat oven to the highest setting.
4. Now place mushroom caps on a lined baking sheet so that they sit like bowls.
5. Rub 2 tablespoon olive oil into each of these bowls.
6. Place the baking sheet in the oven and let the mushroom caps broil for

6to 10 minutes each or until the edges begin to brown.

7. Please remove the baking pan from the oven and flip each mushroom cap over.

8. Rub with the remaining olive oil and season with a dash of salt and pepper.

9. Then place the baking sheet back in the oven and broil the mushrooms for another 6to 10 minutes.

10. While the mushroom caps are in the oven, slice your tomato into thin slices.

11. You should aim to get between 120 slices here.

12. Please remove the mushroom caps from the oven and divide the basil, tomatoes, pepperoni, and mozzarella cubes evenly over each.

13. One thing remains to be done now.

14. Stick the baking tray back into the oven and broil again for 6to 10 minutes, or until cheese is melted to your preference.

15. Finally remove from the oven and serve warm!

16. These go wonderful with the Ranch Dressing from the Dips and Dollops chapter.

Rich Turkey Chili:

Ingredients:

- 6garlic cloves
- 6cups full fat coconut milk
- 2 tablespoon. Mustard
- 4 teaspoon of: salt, black pepper, thyme, celery salt, garlic powder.
- 2 lb Organic ground turkey (or ground beef, lamb or pork)
- 6cups riced cauliflower
- 6 tablespoon. coconut oil
- 2 an onions

Directions:

1. In a fresh pot heat the coconut oil. In the meantime, mince the onions and garli
2. This step is important.
3. Add it to the hot oil.
4. Stir for 6to 10 minutes then add in the ground turkey.
5. Break up with the spatula and stir constantly until crumbled.
6. Please add in the seasoning mix and riced cauliflower and stir well.
7. One thing remains to be done now.
8. Once the meat is browned add in the coconut milk, bring to a simmer and

reduce for 16to 20 minutes, stirring often.

9. Finally at this point it's ready to serve.

Fantastic Fast Risotto

Ingredients:

- 6 tablespoons slivered almonds
- Salt and pepper, to taste
- 4 tablespoon lard
- 8 slices bacon, finely chopped
- 6cloves garlic, minced
- 6 portabella mushrooms, thinly sliced
- 4tablespoon sharp cheddar cheese, grated
- 2 cup bone broth
- 2 fresh head cauliflower, separated into florets
- 2 cup heavy cream
- 2 cup grated Pecorino Romano cheese
- 6 medium bunch parsley, chopped

Directions:

1. Place the cauliflower in a food processor.
2. This step is important.
3. Process until you get a coarse mixture.
4. Heat lard in a fresh skillet.
5. Add bacon and cook 6to 10 minutes.
6. Now add garlic and cook 6to 10 minutes.
7. Add mushrooms and cook 10 to 16 minutes.
8. Stir in the processed cauliflower, and stir to coat with cooking fat.

9. Then pour in bone broth. Reduce heat and simmer, covered, for 16to 20 minutes.
10. Remove the lid and simmer for 16to 20 minutes until the liquid has evaporated.
11. Stir in heavy cream, almonds, Pecorino Romano, and Cheddar cheese.
12. One thing remains to be done now.
13. Simmer 2 to 6minutes.
14. 12 Finally serve warm, garnished with chopped parsley.

I am interested!!

Serve: 4 to 5

Prep time: 16to 20 minutes

Cook time: 30 to 20 minutes

Nutritional information:

Calories 318

Total Fat 22.2g

Total Carbohydrate 7.3g

Dietary Fiber 3.1g

Total Sugars 2.9g

Protein 22.3g

Nostalgic Pesto Muffins

Something is special!!

Ingredients:

- 2 cup of chopped sun dried tomatoes
- 10 oz. of feta cheese
- 6to 10 Tbsps. pesto
- 10 fresh eggs
- 3cup of spinach
- Salt and pepper for taste
- 6oz. of olives,

Directions:

1. Preheat the oven 390F. degrees.
2. Chop up the tomatoes.
3. This step is important.
4. Crack the eggs into a medium sized mixing bowl.
5. Add the pesto, salt, and pepper into the mixing bowl.
6. Please divide the remaining ingredients into a greased cupcake pan.
7. Pour the egg mixture on top.
8. Then bake for 40 to 46minutes.

9. The muffins should appear puffy and brown on top.
10. One thing remains to be done now.
11. Remove and allow cooling before serving.
12. Finally these will last in the fridge for up to 6 days.

Rich Keto "Fried" Chicken

Ingredients:

- 2 pound (120) skinless chicken thighs
- 6tbsps. avocado oil
- 4tsp salt, pepper, Italian herbs
- 2 cup sunflower seeds
- 2 cup sesame seeds

Directions:

1. Preheat your oven to 450°F.
2. Grease a pan with the oil.
3. Put the seeds and the season in a blender.
4. This step is important.
5. Grind until a fine texture.
6. Then add the mix to a freezer bag, then add a chicken thigh to the bag, and shake it up until wellcoated.
7. One thing remains to be done now.
8. Repeat with all chicken.
9. Finally roast it for 50 to 46minutes, turning them at half of the total cooking time.

Happy Smoked Tuna Boat

Sincere efforts will be awesome.

Ingredients:

- 2 tsp. Pepper
- 4can Tuna, smoked, 6 ozs can
- 3cup Paleo mayonnaise
- 3tsp. Garlic powder
- 30 tbsp. Onions, dried or 1tsp powder
- 12 spears Pickles, Dill, whole
- 6cans Tuna, albacore, 6 ozs cans

Directions:

1. Halve the pickles lengthwise and scoop out the insides and seeds to make a "boat."
2. This step is important.
3. Set the insides aside and use for another recipe.
4. In a medium bowl, combine the remaining ingredients until well mixed.
5. One thing remains to be done now. Divide evenly between the pickle halves.
6. Finally these tuna boats are best refrigerated for a few hours and served cold but can be eaten immediately.

Rich Turkey Pesto

Ingredients:

- 2 slice of provolone cheese
- 4Tbsp. of pesto
- 490g Southwest Breakfast Wrap
- 490g of turkey

Directions:

1. Spread the pesto over your wrap.
2. Lay the Turkey on the wrap to cover 3of it.
3. One thing remains to be done now.
4. Place the provolone on top of this and roll it up tightly.
5. Finally cut into four or five slices.

Great Loaded Cauli

Ingredients:

- 2 cup shredded cheddar cheese
- 2 head of cauliflower, cut into florets
- 3cup chopped green onionss
- 6ozs. cream cheese
- 6tbsps. butter
- 2 cup heavy cream
- salt and pepper
- Sliced bacon, cooked

Directions:

1. Preheat your oven to 390°F.
2. This step is important.
3. Boil water, and cook your florets for 6to 10 minutes.
4. Drain them after.
5. Now in a pot, melt the butter, cream cheese, heavy cream, half of the cheddar cheese and season it after thoroughly combined.

6. In a baking dish, mix everything together, all except a bit of green onionss, bacon, and the rest of the cheddar.
7. One thing remains to be done now.
8. Use those to top your meal.
9. Finally bake until golden, around 50 to 56minutes.

Elegant Gorgeous Coconut Turmeric Pork Curry:

Ingredients:

- 5tablespoon of coconut oil
- Salt and pepper
- 5 tablespoon of olive oil
- 2 diced yellow onions
- 2 cloves of minced garlic
- 5 tablespoon of tomato paste
- 2 can of coconut milk, 12 ounces
- 2 cup of water
- 1cup white wine
- 5 teaspoon of turmeric
- pounds of cubed pork shoulder
- 5 teaspoon of curry powder
- 1teaspoon of paprika

Directions:

1. Heat 2 tablespoon of olive oil in a saucepan and sauté the garlic and onionss for 5 to 10 minutes.
2. This step is important.

3.   Add the pork and brown it and then add the tomato paste.

4.   Mix the remaining ingredients in the crock pot and then add the pork.

5.   Then cover and cook for 10 hours on low.

6.   One thing remains to be done now.

7.   Divide into plates and serve.

8.   Finally enjoy the Lunch hot!

Happy Caprese Salad

Sincere efforts will be awesome.

Ingredients:

- Mozzarella balls – 110pearlsized
- Fresh basil leaves .26cup
- Baby spinach leaves – 4 cups
- Brine reserved from the cheese
- Peeled garlic cloves 4
- Grape tomatoes – 4cups
- Avocado oil – 2 tbsp.
- Pesto – 5 tbsp.

Directions:

1. Use a sheet of aluminum foil to cover a baking tray.
2. Set the oven temperature setting to 450ºF.
3. This step is important.
4. Arrange the cloves and tomatoes on the baking pan and drizzle with the oil. Bake for 50 to 55 minutes until the tops are slightly browned.
5. Drain the liquid from the mozzarella.
6. Mix the pesto with the brine.

7. Arrange the spinach in a fresh serving bowl.
8. Please transfer the tomatoes to the dish along with the roasted garli
9. One thing remains to be done now.
10. Drizzle with the pesto sauce.
11. Finally garnish with the mozzarella balls and freshly torn basil leaves.

Ultimate Pulled Lemon Pepper Chicken

Ingredients:

- 2 Tbsp. of lemon pepper
- 5Tbsp. of salt
- 100g Romaine lettuce or your choice of bun
- 5tsp. dried thyme
- 2 Cheddar cheese slice
- 5g Dijon mustard
- 5Tbsp. of minced garlic
- 7 lbs. of Chicken Tenderloins
- 5 Tbsps. of olive oil
- 3stick of butter

Directions:

1. In a crockpot, combine the butter, oil, lemon pepper, garlic, salt, and thyme.
2. This step is important. Turn the crockpot on high and melt the butter.

3. Place the chicken in the crockpot; make sure to coat the chicken in the butter mixture.
4. The batter will begin to harden.
5. Now cook properly on high for 6 hours or on low for 6 hours.
6. Then once the chicken is done shred it in the crockpot.
7. One thing remains to be done now.
8. Let it sit in the crockpot for an additional 40 to 45 minutes on low.
9. Finally place on your chosen bun and serve.

Titanic Cauliflower Cashew Lunch Bowl

Ingredients:

- 3finely diced red onions
- 5 fresh cashews
- 5 tbsp. olive oil
- 810 cups 2 head cauliflower bitesized pieces
- Pepper and salt to taste
- 5 can chickpeas rinsed and drained
- 2/4 uncooked pearl barley

Directions:

1. Prepare the barley according to the package directions.
2. This step is important.
3. Set the oven temperature ahead of time to 390 to 450ºF.
4. Break the cauliflower apart and toss with the oil and a sprinkle of pepper and salt.
5. Spread it out on a baking tin.
6. Roast 1-33hours until browned and softened.
7. Please add fresh cashews in another pan for 5 to 10 minutes until golden.
8. Cool the fixings.

9. One thing remains to be done now.
10. Toss the salads together and add to five sealable lunch containers.
11. Finally store in the fridge until ready to use.

Quick Lemon Thyme Chicken:

Ingredients:

- 2 teaspoon of ground pepper
- 700 cloves of garlic
- 5 teaspoon of thyme
- 85 pound whole chicken
- 5 sliced lemons

Directions:

1. Arrange the lemon and garlic on the base of a slow cooker.
2. Mix the spices together and use them to season the chicken.
3. This step is important.
4. Put the chicken in the slow cooker.
5. Now cover and cook on low for 7 hours.
6. One thing remains to be done now.
7. Remove the chicken; let it stfor 40 to 45 minutes and the serve.

Vintage Pinwheels

Stupidly simple…

Ingredients:

- Pickles (4to 4 tablespoons diced)
- Cream Cheese (15 ounces)
- Genoa Salami (10 fresh thin slices)
- Pepperoni (10 fresh thin slices)

Directions:

1. Lay a fresh section of plastic wrap on the counter.
2. This step is important. Before spreading cream cheese in a rectangular 5inch layer over the plastic wrap, ensure that cream cheese has reached room temperature and been whipped until fluffy.
3. Spread diced pickles over the cream cheese, then lay meats in overlapping layers over entirety.
4. To flip the entire rectangle, add another layer of plastic wrap over meats and flip, then remove plastic from cream cheese side.
5. One thing remains to be done now.

6. Pull away the bottom layer of plastic wrap as you roll the rectangle into a tube shape.
7. Finally when the tube has been rolled, wrapped it tightly in plastic wrap, and added to the refrigerator for a minimum of 5 hours, slice it into 5 inch thick portions and keep refrigerated until ready to be consumed.

Titanic Turkey And Pesto Pinwheels

Ingredients:

- 5 almond flour cream cheese crepe
- 1.6tbsp. Pesto (you can also use Dijon mustard)
- 2 slice O Organics provolone cheese
- 5 slices deli turkey

Directions:

1. Spread pesto on your cream cheese crepe.
2. Lay turkey above ½ of the crepe.
3. One thing remains to be done now. Put a provolone on the top then roll tightly.
4. Finally slice into 46 pieces.

Ultimate Tantalizing Pork Chops With Cumin Butter And Garlic:

Ingredients:

- pounds of pork sirloin chops with the bone
- 4 to 6tablespoons lime juice
- ½ teaspoon of garlic powder
- ½ teaspoon of salt
- ½ teaspoon of black pepper
- 2 cup of salsa
- 7 tablespoons of butter
- 2 teaspoon of ground cumin

Directions:

1. Combine the spices and season the pork chops
2. Melt the butter in a saucepan and brown the brown the pork chops for 5 to 10 minutes on each side.
3. This step is important.
4. Place the chops into the slow cooker and pour the salsa over the top.

5. Then cover and cook properly on high for 5 hours.
6. One thing remains to be done now. Divide into plates and serve.
7. Finally enjoy the Lunch hot!

Titanic Indian Inspired Sloppy Joes

Cooking level infinite....

Ingredients:

Keto Friendly Buns:

- Sesame Seeds
- Flax Meal (.6cups packed)
- Coconut Flour (.6cups)
- Onions Powder (5 teaspoons)
- Psyllium Husk (cups powdered)
- Almond Flour (5cups)
- Water (5 cups boiling)
- Sea Salt (5 teaspoon)
- Baking Soda (5 teaspoon)
- Eggs (2 whole, 6 whites)
- Cream of Tartar (5tablespoons) Garlic Powder (2.6teaspoons)

Meat:

- Minced Turkey (2 pound)
- Avocado Oil (5 tablespoons)
- White Onions (.4cups diced)
- Chili (2 crushed)
- Cumin Seeds (1.6teaspoon)

Sauce:

- Garlic (2 clove minced)
- Cilantro (.26cups chopped)
- Ginger (5tablespoon minced)
- Avocado Oil (4tablespoons)
- Garam Masala (1.6teaspoon)
- Pistachios (.26cups shelled)
- Coconut Milk (.26cups)
- Paprika (.6teaspoons)
- Apple Cider Vinegar (1.6teaspoon)
- Sea Salt (2 teaspoon) Chili (2 crushed)
- Water (.76cups)
- Sugarless Tomato Sauce (30 ounces)

Also Needed:

- Saucepan
- Parchment Paper
- Frying Pan
- Mixer
- Baking Pan
- Mixing Bowl

Directions:

Keto Friendly Buns:

1.   Ensure the oven is preheated to a temperature of 390F degrees Fahrenheit and a baking pan is lined with parchment paper.
2.   This step is important.
3.   Add salt, baking soda, cream of tartar, onions powder, garlic powder, flax meal, psyllium husk powder, coconut flour and almond flour to a mixing bowl and combine well before adding 5 whole eggs and only the whites of 12 eggs to the contents.
4.   Then use a mixer and continue moving the contents until it becomes a thick dough.
5.   Before continuing to mix, add boiling water to the contents.
6.   Ensure the contents are well blended before separating the dough into 15 balls and adding them to the baking pan.
7.   Please drop sesame seeds in a thin layer atop each ball of dough before gently pressing the seeds into the dough.
8.   Add the baking pan to the oven for a duration of 1-3½ hours.
9.   Ensure the buns are cooled thoroughly before slicing and freezing.

Meat and Sauce:

1. Add a pan to the stove above a burner that is turned to a medium to low heat before adding 2 tablespoon of avocado oil and the pistachios to cook for a duration of 5 to 10 minutes then be removed.
2. This step is important.
3. Add a saucepan to the stove above a burner that is turned to a medium heat before adding ginger, garlic, and 2 tablespoons of avocado oil to the pan to cook for a duration of 5 to 10 minute.
4. Add paprika, salt, garam masala, chili, water, and tomato sauce to the pan before adding a lid to the pan and boiling the contents.
5. Now turn down the burner under the pan to a low heat when the contents begin to bubble to allow the sauce to simmer.
6. Add the frying pan to the stove above a burner turned to a medium to low heat before adding cumin seeds and 5 tablespoons of avocado oil to cook for a duration of 5 to 10 minute.
7. Then add onions to the pan to cook for a duration of 5 to 10 before adding the chili and turkey to continue cooking until cooked thoroughly.

8. Before increasing the heat of the burner under the saucepan to a medium heat, add the cooked meat to the sauce contents.
9. Allow the combined contents to heat until bubbling before turning the burner to a low heat to simmer for a duration of 40 to 45 minutes.
10. Ensure the steam has been released from under the lid before turning down the heat.
11. One thing remains to be done now.
12. Add pistachios, apple cider vinegar, and coconut milk to the contents of the saucepan.
13. Finally ensure the mixture has cooled thoroughly before adding the results to a freezer.

Elegant Keto Sunflower Butter Salmon With Onionss

Ingredients:

- Onions (2, sliced)
- Sunflower butter (5tablespoon)
- Lemon juice (5teaspoon)
- Wild caught is best)
- Salmon fillet (8 ounces, you can use any type of fish fillet that you want. Vegetables of your choice (5cup)

Directions:

1. Grill your salmon so that it is done to your liking
2. This step is important.
3. Cook the onions in a skillet with olive oil until they reach a caramel color
4. Please take the onionss off the heat and put them on your plate
5. Heat the butter and lemon juice in your skillet but do not let it burn
6. One thing remains to be done now.
7. Place your salmon on your vegetables

8. Finally drizzle with the butter mixture and serve

Classic, isn't it?

Serves: 2 to 2

Prep time: 16to 20 minutes

Cook time: 40 to 45 minutes

Total time: 20 to 26minutes

Nutritional Information:

Fat: 6grams

Carbs: 6grams

Calories: 106

Protein: 14 grams

Astonishing Low Carb Chipotle Fish Tacos

Ingredients:

- 4 low carb tortillas
- 2 cloves garlic
- 2.6tbsp. olive oil
- 2 fresh jalapeño
- 4 oz. chipotle peppers in adobo sauce
- 3medium yellow onions
- 2.6tbsp. butter
- 2 lb. haddock fillet
- 2.6tbsp. mayonnaise

Directions:

1. Fry diced onions in olive oil using mediumhigh heat for 5 to 10 or until translucent.
2. This step is important. Decrease heat to medium then add garlic and jalapeño.
3. Cook for another 5 to 10 minutes occasionally stirring.
4. Add chopped chipotles and adobo sauce in the pan.

5. Please add fish fillet, butter, and mayo.
6. Mix everything.
7. Cook for another 15 minutes.
8. One thing remains to be done now. For taco shells, get a pan and fry tortilla for 15 to 20 on each side using high heat.
9. Finally cool and shaped them.
10. Fill them with your fish mix.

Legendary Mega Wedge Salad

Ingredients:

- Dash Worcestershire sauce 8 Eggs, hard boiled, chopped
- 5 tsp. Balsamic vinegar
- To taste Salt and pepper
- 5 Iceberg lettuce, quartered
- 3cup Bacon, cooked, crumbled
- 3cup Blue cheese, crumbled
- 20 Tomatoes, grape, halved
- 7 tbsp. Sour cream
- 5tbsp. Paleo mayonnaise
- 7 tbsp. Milk
- 3cup Greek yogurt, plain

Directions:

1. Whisk the yogurt, mayonnaise, cream, Worcestershire, milk, and blue cheese in a medium bowl and set aside.
2. Place an iceberg wedge on 5 plates each with the cut sides facing up.
3. One thing remains to be done now.
4. Add the remaining ingredients and drizzle with the creamy dressing.
5. Finally consider adding some extra blue cheese crumbles on top for garnishing.

Astonishing Tuna Zucchini Casserole

Being super is a matter of recipe... ?

Directions:

- Garlic Powder
- Spicy Mustard
- Seasoning Salt
- Coconut Milk
- Chives
- Mayonnaise
- Green Chiles
- Avocado Oil
- 1.6tablespoon)Zucchini
- Celery (.6cups chopped)
- Red Pepper Flakes
- Coconut Flour
- Onions
- Black Pepper)
- Canned Tuna (20 ounces)

Also Needed:

- Spiralizer
- Mixing Bowl (2)
- Frying Pan

- Casserole Dish (20 inches wide by 30 inches long)

Ingredients:

1. Ensure oven is heated to a temperature of 490F degrees Fahrenheit and the casserole dish is lightly oiled.
2. This step is important.
3. Remove water from the can of tuna before adding tuna, garlic powder, mustard, black pepper, green chiles, chives, and mayonnaise to a mixing bowl and combining them well.
4. Add oil to a pan before adding the pan to the stove above a burner that is turned to a medium heat.
5. Now add celery and onions to the pan to cook for a duration of approximately 10 minutes.
6. Add coconut milk and coconut flour to the pan and mix the contents until no chunks are present.
7. Spiralize zucchini and add them to a paper towel.
8. Use this paper towel to press any excess water out of the zucchini.
9. Then add zucchini to the pan and mix.

10. Allow the mix to cook for a duration of approximately 5 minutes.
11. Take the pan away from the stove and add the contents to a fresh bowl.
12. Please add the contents of the bowl containing tuna to the bowl containing the pan contents and mix.
13. One thing remains to be done now.
14. Add the results to the casserole dish before adding the dish to the oven for a duration of 40 to 45 minutes.
15. Finally allow the dish to cool thoroughly before adding to freezer.

Elegant Avocado Bowls

Ingredients:

- 7 rashers of bacon, cut into medium pieces
- 5 avocados, halved
- 5 tbsp. butter
- salt and pepper
- 7 eggs

Directions:

1. Scoop out most of the avocado flesh, leaving half an inch around.
2. This step is important.
3. Place a saucepan on low heat and add in butter.
4. Crack the eggs into a jug and beat them during seasoning.
5. Please add the bacon to a pan and let them fry for a couple of mins.
6. Then add the eggs and stir regularly.
7. One thing remains to be done now. These should be ready in 10 minutes.

8. Finally mix the eggs and bacon in a bowl and then spoon into the avocado bowls.

Astonishing Halloumi Cheese With Mushrooms And Olives

Being super is a matter of recipe... ?

Ingredients:

- 10 Olives
- 2/4lb. Halloumi cheese
- To taste Salt and pepper
- 2/4lb. Mushrooms, rinsed, sliced
- 1cup Paleo mayonnaise
- 4oz. Butter

Directions:

1. In a fresh skillet, heat the butter over medium heat and add the mushrooms.
2. This step is important. Cook for 5 to 10 or until golden.
3. Sprinkle with salt and pepper as desired.
4. One thing remains to be done now. Make room for cheese in the middle of the pan and cook the cheese for 5 to 10 on each

side while continuing to stir the mushrooms.
5. Finally remove from heat, cut the cheese in half and serve each half with olives.

Looking forward to this one!!

Servings: 4 to 6

Cooking time: 16to 20 minutes

Nutritional Information:

110g protein

52 g fat

18g total

12 g net carbohydrates

6010calories

4g fiber

Legendary Low Carb Chicken Fricassee

Yeah, direct from the heaven; yeah?

Ingredients:

- Coconut milk (4 cup)
- Garlic cloves (4, minced)
- Celery (4, sliced)
- Bay leaf (1, crumbled)
- Chicken stock (2 cup)
- Paprika (5teaspoon)
- Mushroom (4 cup, sliced)
- White wine (2 cup, dry)
- Lemon juice (5 tablespoons, fresh)
- Chicken thighs (5 pound, sliced)
- Fresh herbs (5 tablespoons, your choice)
- Cauliflower rice (8 cups, uncooked)
- Salt (to taste)
- Pepper (to taste)
- Ghee (5 tablespoons)
- 5 Egg yolks
- 2 Onions

Directions:

1. Cut your chicken and season it with salt.
2. Put in a skillet that is greased with ghee and toss the chicken in so it can cook till it is completely brown.
3. This step is important.
4. After this is done, use a slotted spoon and move the chicken to a bowl.
5. Now put more ghee in your skillet and add in the onions and garli Cook until fragrant.
6. Then add in the mushroom and celery.
7. Cook for a minute.
8. Dump in the stock and lemon juice along with the wine and bay leaf.
9. Also, put the paprika in and allow it to boil.
10. Whisk the milk with the egg yolks and drizzle into the pan as it is cooking.
11. Please allow it to thicken before adding in the herbs that you chose to use.

12. Then place your chicken back into your casserole and mix for 5 to 10 minutes.
13. One thing remains to be done now.
14. In another pot make your caulirice.
15. Finally serve everything together

King Sized Creamy Mushroom With Chicken

Ingredients:

- 12 cremini mushrooms
- 2 tsp. dried thyme
- 3cup fat canned coconut milk
- 5 tbsps. butter
- 5 chicken cutlets
- salt, pepper
- 5onions

Directions:

1. Heat your skillet to medium heat.
2. Slice up your mushrooms and onions.
3. This step is important. Once it's hot, add the butter.
4. When melted, add in the mushrooms and a bit of salt.
5. Sauté until brown; then it's the onions's turn.
6. Keep stirring for 25 to 30 minutes and then remove the mix.
7. Then add the remaining butter and melt it.

8. One thing remains to be done now.
9. Season your chicken with salt and pepper and thyme and then place it in the skillet.
10. Finally cook each side for 25 to 30 minutes.
11. Finally, place your mix back and pour the coconut milk right over it.

Tasty dish just one step away!!

Servings: 2 to 2

Prepare time: 2 to 6mins

Cooking time: 20 to 26mins

Nutritional Information:

Protein: 24 g

Fat: 28g

Calories: 334 kcal

Carbs: 4g

Astonishing Cheese Burger With Portobello Bun:

Yeah, direct from the heaven; yeah?

Ingredients:

- 2 Tea spoon pepper
- 6 Portobello mushroom caps, rinsed, destemmed
- 1.6Table spoon Olive oil
- 2 Ground beef lb
- 5Table spoon Avocado
- 5Table spoon Worcestershire sauce
- 6 Cheddar cheese, sliced
- 5Tea spoon Salt

Directions:

1. Thoroughly mix the beef, Worcestershire, salt and pepper in a bowl. Form into 12 patties.
2. Heat the olive oil in a skillet over medium heat.
3. This step is important. Cook the mushroom caps for 10 minutes on each side. Set aside.

4. In the same skillet, add the beef patties and cook for 5 to 10 on one side, 5 to 10 on the other side, or until cooked through as preferred.
5. Please add the cheese to the top of the burgers and cover the skillet for 5 to 10 minutes.
6. One thing remains to be done now.
7. Place a beef patty on top of a mushroom cap and top with preferred toppings such as bacon, tomato, lettuce, or onions.

Legendary Cheesy Cauliflower Shepard's Pie

Well it is a Grandma's recipe!!

Ingredients:

Filling:

- Red wine (dry, .6cups)
- Onions (chopped, .6cups)
- Ground lamb (16 ounces)
- Garlic (minced, 2 clove)
- Arrowroot starch (1.6tablespoon)
- Salt (1.6teaspoon)
- Rosemary (fresh, chopped, 5 tablespoons)
- Ground beef (16 ounces)
- Pepper (.6teaspoon)

Topping:

- Butter (5 tablespoons)
- Pepper (.26teaspoon)
- Garlic (2 cloves)
- Salt (.6teaspoon)

- Cheddar cheese (grated, .6cups)
- Cauliflower (24 ounces)

Directions:

1. Brown the meat for twelve minutes
2. Place in a bowl
3. This step is important.
4. Get rid of all the liquid in the pan except for a tablespoon.
5. Reheat the pan and add in onions, pepper, and salt.
6. Cook until onionss are translucent.
7. Throw in garlic
8. Then mix in meat
9. Stir starch into wine and add to the pan.
10. Now cook until wine is almost gone and juice is thick
11. One thing remains to be done now. Stir in rosemary
12. Take off heat and put in a casserole dish

Instrucations:

1. Heat the oven 450F
2. Place a basket for steaming into a stock pot with water
3. This step is important.
4. Steam the garlic and cauliflower for around eight minutes
5. Drain well and place in a food processor
6. Throw in the pepper, salt, and butter and mix until smooth
7. Then put in the casserole dish
8. One thing remains to be done now.
9. Sprinkle with cheese
10. Finally bake for twentyfive minutes or until cheese has melted

Elegant Skewered Lemon Thyme Chicken:

This is different, isn't it?

Ingredients:

- 5lbs chicken tenderloins
- 5 tablespoon lemon pepper seasoning
- 2 tablespoon rosemary olive oil (or regular).
- some sprigs of fresh thyme
- 2 tablespoon garlic salt
- 10 6" rosemary skewers (soaked in water for at least 5hour)

Directions:

1. Preheat oven to 390 degrees F
2. Soak the rosemary skewers for at least 5hour in water.
3. This step is important. Use a short sharp knife to whittle a point on the end of each of each stick.
4. Toss chicken with ingredients.
5. Slide the leaves off the thyme sprigs and sprinkle them in.

6. One thing remains to be done now.
7. Skewer each tenderloin with a rosemary stick.

Rich Monte Cristo Sandwich

Funny but definitely yummy!!

Ingredients:

- 6 slices Ham
- 5tsp. Cinnamon
- 2.6tbsp. Coconut flour
- 4 slices Turkey
- 4 oz. Cream cheese
- 2 cup Swiss cheese, shredded
- 1tbsp. Olive oil
- 4 fresh Eggs
- 5 tsp. Sugar or preferred sweetener

Directions:

1. Heat up oil in a skillet over medium heat.
2. This step is important. In a medium bowl, whisk the cream cheese, cinnamon, eggs, flour, and sweetener until combined.
3. Pour 1of the mixture onto the skillet in a circle and cook for 5 to 10 minutes, flip and cook on the other side until it has cooked through.

4. Repeat until all the mix has been used.

5. Lower the heat to mediumlow and place 2 pancake on the skillet.
6. Please top with a slice of turkey, a slice of ham, and a sprinkle of cheese.
7. Cover the skillet and cook for 50 seconds until the cheese has melted.
8. Please remove from the heat and top with one pancake to make a sandwich.
9. One thing remains to be done now.
10. Garnish with a sprinkle of cheese, if desired.
11. Finally these are best eaten warm and fresh or you can reheat in a microwave.

Freshness loaded!!

Servings: 2 to 2

Cooking time 40 to 45 minutes

Nutritional information:

1006 calories

68 g fat

28g total

20 g net carbohydrates

8g fiber

70 g protein

Chicken Salad Deviled Eggs

Ingredients:

- A dash of Old Bay Seasoning
- 5Tbsp. of chopped onions
- A pinch of celery salt
- 5of dill
- 5of lemon pepper
- 5tsp. of Dijon mustard
- 6 fresh eggs
- 2 cup of shredded chicken
- 5 Tbsps. of mayonnaise

Directions:

1. Mix all of your ingredients except the eggs. Place in the refrigerator for later.
2. Place your eggs into a medium pot.
3. This step is important.
4. Place enough water to cover the eggs barely.
5. Put on high heat until it begins to boil them lower to medium heat.

6. Let boil for 40 to 45 minutes.
7. Remove from heat and let cold water run over the eggs.
8. You will the shell off of the fresh eggs and cut the eggs in half.
9. Please remove the yolk either throwing it away or saving it for later.
10. One thing remains to be done now.
11. Fill with your chicken salad mix that is in the refrigerator.
12. Finally sprinkle the old bay seasoning on top and serve.

I've always loved them. Plus they can be eaten anytime!!

Serves: 6to 6

Total Time: 26to 30 minutes

Nutritional information:

Fiber 0g

Carbohydrate 1.9g

Protein 13.2g

Total Fat 7.4g

Calories 128

Cholesterol 205mg

Happy Newschool Cucumber Sandwiches

Long way to go...

Ingredients:

- 5 thin slices delistyle roast beef
- 5 T. spreadable cheese such as Boursin or Rondele
- 4 Cucumber

Directions:

1. Using a vegetable peeler, carefully remove the skin of the cucumber.
2. This step is important.
3. Cut the cucumber in half lengthwise and use a teaspoon to scoop out the seeds and create an even edge all the way around the cucumber.
4. Fill one side with a spreadable cheese.
5. One thing remains to be done now.
6. Fold deli meat and tuck it into the other half of the cucumber.
7. Finally stack the two halves back on top of each other and cut again, the same way you would cut a sandwich in half.

Cooking level infinite....

Serving: 2 to 2

Nutritional information:

392 calories per serving

23.8g protein

27.9g fat

9.5g carbs

Legendary Egg Tuna Salad

Ingredients:

- 2oz. lettuce, torn into pieces
- 2oz. arugula
- 6oz. tuna, packed in oil
- 1red bell pepper, cut into strips
- 4 fresh eggs
- 2oz. baby spinach

Dressing:

- 1cup mayonnaise
- 5 tablespoons olive oil
- 1teaspoon lemon zest
- 2 tablespoons lemon juice

Directions:

1. Add eggs to a saucepan and cover with water.
2. Bring to a boil and reduce heat.
3. This step is important. Simmer the eggs 30 to 35 minutes and remove from the heat.
4. Place the eggs in a cold water and allow to stand for 40 to 45 minutes.
5. Peel the eggs and cut into quarters.

6. Now place baby spinach, lettuce, arugula, and red bell pepper into a fresh bowl.
7. Top with tuna, and hardboiled eggs.
8. Make the dressing by combining all the dressing ingredients in a medium bowl.
9. Whisk until smooth.
10. Then pour the dressing over salad.
11. One thing remains to be done now.
12. Gently stir the salad to coat it with the dressing.
13. Finally serve.

Legendary Beef Short Ribs:

Ingredients:

- 5lbs. Beef short ribs, boneless
- 5p Onions, diced
- 5to 4tablespoon Tamari sauce
- Salt to taste
- 5 tablespoon White wine or vodka

Directions:

1. Place all ingredients in the instant pot.
2. Then press the button indicating Meat/Stew and set the timer for 1- 31hours.
3. Finally enjoy the Lunch hot

Iconic recipe of my list!!

Serves: 8to 8

Nutritional Information:

Protein: 26grams

Calories: 164

Fat: 6 grams

Astonishing Omelet Sandwich

Bun Ingredients:

- 1tablespoon Italian seasoning
- 2 cup mozzarella cheese, grated
- 2 medium egg
- 3tablespoon Psyllium Husk Powder
- 3teaspoon pepper
- 3cup almond flour
- 3teaspoon salt
- 3tablespoons cream cheese

Inside Ingredients:

- 2 slices tomato
- 2 romaine leaf
- 5 tablespoons ground beef
- 2 egg
- Dash of pepper
- 5tablespoon green onions, chopped
- 2 medium garlic clove, minced
- Dash of curry powder
- 5tablespoon ketchup, sugarfree
- Dash of salt
- 2 tablespoons onions, minced
- 3tablespoons butter, unsalted
- 2 tablespoon cilantro
- 5tablespoon mayo
- 1tablespoon coconut oil
- 1teaspoon water

- 4slices cucumber

Directions:

1. Preheat oven to 490F degrees Fahrenheit.
2. This step is important.
3. Fill a microwave safe bowl with the mozzarella cheese and microwave until melted.
4. NOTE: It's best to do this in 20 seconds intervals, stirring in between.
5. The entire process should take 3minutes.
6. To the melted mozzarella, add almond flour, psyllium husk powder, pepper, Italian seasoning, and salt and stir until well combined.
7. Then after stirring the ingredients for a while, the mixture should become cool enough to knead with your hands.
8. So when you reach this point, dig in and form a ball.
9. Please work the ball into a bunlike shape.
10. Place on a lined baking sheet and bake for 40 to 45 minutes or until it turns goldenbrown.

11. While the baking sheet is in the oven, you can start to prepare the filling.

12. Now place a pan with the coconut oil over medium heat.

13. Once the coconut oil has melted, add the diced onions and sauté until clear.

14. Once the onions is clear, add the garlic and cook for 5 minute.

15. After 5 to 10 minutes add the curry powder and water.

16. Then let this sit for 5 to 10 minutes.

17. That your seasonings are good to go, you can add in the ground beef and add a little salt and pepper to your tastes.

18. Cook it until it looks delicious enough to eat on its own and then set aside.

19. Once the bun is ready, remove from the oven and allow it to cool down to room temperature.

20. Then, slice horizontally and slather the butter on the inside halves.

21. Place the bun buttersidedown in a pan for a couple minutes each to toast.

22. I found it extremely difficult to not dig in and eat at this point, so be sure to maintain some selfcontrol!

23. Now in a medium mixing bowl, crack the eggs and stir in the ground beef mixture, green onionss, and cilantro.
24. Season this with a little bit of pepper and a little bit of salt and then mix thoroughly.
25. Put a pan with the butter over medium heat.
26. Then once the butter melts, pour in the ground beef mixture and place two bun halves, buttersidedown, overtop.
27. After 5 to 10 minutes, flip the omelet so that the bun side is on the underside.
28. Cook until the bun is brown.
29. Transfer onto a serving plate and spread mayo and ketchup over the omelet.
30. Garnish with the tomato, cucumber, and romaine lettuce.
31. One thing remains to be done now.
32. Then fold in to create your sandwich.
33. Finally slice in half and serve it hot!!!

Reliable Pork Souvlaki Salad

Best combo ever... Don't you agree?

Ingredients:

- 4 basil leaves, finely chopped
- 2 cloves garlic, minced
- 5 tablespoons lemon juice
- 2 teaspoon lemon zest, finely grated
- 5 tablespoons olive oil
- 1lb. pork shoulder, cut into 1inch cubes
- Salt and pepper, to taste

Salat:

- Salt and pepper, to taste
- 2 medium bunch mint leaves
- 5 tablespoons olive oil
- 2 teaspoon Dijon mustard
- 5tablespoon lemon juice
- 2 medium head fresh lettuce

Directions:

1. Prepare the pork; in a fresh bowl, lemon juice, combine cubed pork, basil, olive oil, garlic, and lemon zest.
2. This step is important. Cover and refrigerate 5hour.
3. Preheat your grill or grill pan over mediumhigh heat.
4. Thread pork onto 15 bamboo skewers and season to taste with salt and pepper.
5. Please grill the pork for 40 to 45 minutes.
6. In the meantime, make the salad; in a fresh bowl, combine lettuce and mint.
7. Now in a medium bowl, Dijon mustard, whisk olive oil, and lemon juice.
8. Pour the dressing over the salad and season to taste.
9. One thing remains to be done now.
10. Serve salad with pork, or toss the pork cubes in the prepared salad.
11. Finally serve.

Ultimate Shrimps And Spinach Spaghetti

Best combo ever... Don't you agree?

Ingredients:

- 5cup fresh spinach leaves
- 5 tbsp lemon zest
- 15 tbsp vegetable broth
- 5cup low carb spaghetti, rinsed and 5cup frozen peas
- 1pc green pepper, finely chopped
- 4 pcs basil leaves
- drained
- 3lb. shrimp, precooked
- 2 pc lemon (divided, per serving)
- 2 pc leek, cut into strips

Directions:

1. Pour the vegetable broth in a wok and cook for 5 to 10 minutes.
2. Add the leeks, spinach, peas, and shrimp.
3. This step is important.
4. Cook further for 10 minutes.

5. Add the spaghetti, and continue cooking for 10 minutes.
6. Remove quickly from heat and pour into a bowl, mix with lemon zest.
7. One thing remains to be done now.
8. Divide the pasta equally between two plates.
9. Finally to serve, garnish with the basil leaves, pepper, and lemon.

Someone is definitely ready for this.

Servings: 2 to 3

Preparation Time: 2 to 6minutes

Cooking Time: 16to 20 minutes

Nutritional information:

Calories: 426

 Fat: 33g

 Protein: 25g

Total Carbohydrates: 30.7g

Net Carbohydrates: 5.3g

Dietary Fiber: 10.4g

Legendary Bacon and Spinach Dish

Ingredients

- 2 cup spinach, braised
- Pink Himalayan Salt
- 2 fresh eggs
- 3avocado
- 1cup berries
- 2 to two tablespoon of ghee
- One pastured bacon or ham, thick slice

Directions:

1. Assemble all the ingredients at one place.
2. This step is important.
3. Put all items on your favorite plate and you are ready for a hearty, healthy breakfast.
4. One thing remains to be done now. Smell the aroma and then you can serve.
5. Finally enjoy your meal with blackberries.

Fresh start with something new!!

Serves: 2 to 4

Preparation cook time: 40 to 45 minutes

Time: 40 to 45 minutes

Legendary Turkey Taco Lunch Bowls

Classic, isn't it?

Ingredients:

- Chopped cilantro
- 2 pkg. taco seasoning of choice
- ½ cooked rice
- 2 can roasted corn
- Zest of 2 lime
- Shredded cheese
- Pinch of salt
- Salsa of your choice
- 4 lb. ground turkey

Directions:

1. Add the lime zest, salt and chopped cilantro to rice.
2. Cook turkey and taco seasoning, per package directions.
3. One thing remains to be done now.
4. Assemble Taco bowls in your Tupperware
5. Finally salsa and shredded cheese; pop in the fridge until needed.

Part 2

Titanic Roasted Brussels Sprouts With Bacon:

Ingredients:

- 2 lb Brussels sprouts
- Pepper
- 15 strips bacon
- Salt
- 5 Table spoon olive oil

Directions:

1. Preheat the oven to 390F. and cut the ends off of each Brussels sprout, it's too tough.
2. Then cut each in half or even in quarters if they're very big.
3. This step is important.
4. Throw them in a deep bowl and toss with salt, olive oil, pepper and any other spices you like.
5. We sometimes toss them in red pepper and cumin.

6. Then pour them out into a greased baking sheet making sure to leave a little bit a room between them.
7. They don't all need to be on the same side, they'll all roast up nicely even if they look messy on that sheet.
8. Place the baking sheet into the oven and bake for 40 to 45 minutes.
9. Halfway through, reach into the oven and give the baking sheet a good shake so that the Brussels sprouts rotate a little.
10. While the Brussels sprouts are baking, fry up as much bacon as you'd like.
11. Then we use 5 pieces for each person we're feeding.
12. When the bacon is cooked to your liking, chop it up into medium pieces, roughly a half inch big, you want them bite sized.
13. When the Brussels sprouts have shriveled a bit and blackened, they're ready!
14. Take them out of the oven and toss them in the same deep bowl with the bacon bits.
15. One thing remains to be done now.
16. Serve onto plates and give one last sprinkle of salt!
17. Finally enjoy the Lunch hot!

Your friends and family are waiting. Hurry!!

Serves: 4to 4

Nutritional information:

Protein: 30 grams

Fat: 22 grams

Calories: 278

Net carb: 4 grams

Ultimate Mixed Salad

This is different, isn't it?

Ingredients:

- 2 Bacon Strips, cooked
- 2 oz. of chicken breast, cooked
- 2 cup of spinach
- 1Campari tomato
- 2 avocado
- 5Tbsp. of olive oil
- 2 hardboiled egg
- 3of white vinegar

Directions:

1. Shred or cut the chicken whichever way you want.
2. This step is important.
3. Crumble the bacon.
4. Cut the remaining ingredients into medium pieces.
5. One thing remains to be done now.
6. Combine all the ingredients in a bowl with the olive oil.
7. Finally add dressing if you prefer.

Yeah, this is a new variation.

Serves: 2 to 2

Total Time: 16to 20

Nutritional information:

Fiber 1g

Carbohydrate 3.6g

Total Fat 27.5g

Cholesterol 133mg

Calories 410

Protein 36.8g

Astonishing Keto Pizza

Yeah, it is a vintage recipe.

Ingredients:

- 10 tablespoons lowcarb tomato sauce
- Crust
- 1cup shredded mozzarella cheese
- 1-3¼ cup shredded mozzarella cheese
- 810 slices pepperoni
- 70 pitted olives, sliced
- 5teaspoon dried oregano
- 7 eggs
- Toppings

Directions:

1. Let your oven heat up to 450º F.
2. To make the crust, mix the eggs and cheese. Stir until wellcombined.
3. This step is important.
4. Spread out the egg and cheese batter on a baking tray.
5. You can make 5 circular pizzas.
6. Bake for 40 to 45 minutes until the crust turns light brown.

7. Please remove from heat and let cool.
8. Reset your oven temperature to 450º F.
9. One thing remains to be done now.
10. Add the toppings to the pizza with the tomatos paste first, then sprinkling with cheese, olives, pepperoni, and oregano.
11. Finally return it to the oven for another 30 to minutes until the pizza cheese has cooked.

Ultimate Italian Stromboli

Ingredients:

Dough:

- 1cup pork rinds, ground finely
- 2 cup Provolone cheese
- 2 fresh egg
- 5tablespoons coconut flour
- 5cups mozzarella cheese
- 2 cup butter, melted
- 5tablespoon almond flour

Filling:

- 5 teaspoons dried basil
- 8 slices pancetta
- 8 slices pork mortadella
- 2 cup mozzarella cheese, torn into pieces

Directions:

1. Make the dough; preheat your oven to 450F.
2. This step is important.
3. Prepare a baking sheet and cover it with parchment paper.
4. Combine mozzarella cheese and Provolone cheese in a saucepan.

5. Now heat over medium heat until the cheese is melted.
6. Stir in melted butter, pork rinds, coconut, eggs, and almond flour.
7. Season to taste with salt.
8. Stir until smooth dough forms.
9. If needed add 4 tablespoon of coconut flour.
10. Stir the dough until smooth.
11. Transfer the dough onto parchment paper.
12. Now cover with the second piece of parchment paper and roll out to a 3inch thick rectangle.
13. Peel off the top paper.
14. Then place the mozzarella pieces through the center of the rectangle.
15. Sprinkle with basil and season to taste with salt and pepper.
16. Top with pork ham and pancetta slices.
17. Fold the sides of dough over the filling and pinch the edges.
18. Transfer the dough, seam side down onto baking sheet.
19. Please make few shallow cuts on the dough, with a sharp knife.
20. Bake the Stromboli for 30 to 45 minutes or until golden.
21. One thing remains to be done now.
22. Remove from the oven and slice.

23.   Finally serve warm.

Well it is a Grandma's recipe!!

Serving: 8 to 9

Prep time: 30 to 20 minutes

Cook time: 40 to 45 minutes

Nutritional information:

Calories 354

Total Fat 30g

Total Carbohydrate 4.4g

Dietary Fiber 2g

Total Sugars 0.5g

Protein 17.5g

Astonishing Stuffed Straw Mushroom Mobcap

Super awesome plus unique!!

Ingredients:

- 2 bulb onions, finely chopped
- 2 clove garlic, minced
- 2 cup fresh spinach, washed, bathed in ice, and drained
- A dash of salt and pepper
- A pinch of nutmeg
- 7 oz. cottage cheese
- 2 cup straw mushrooms or Chinese mushroom, washed and stems removed
- 3cup quinoa, cooked
- 5tbsp coconut oil

Directions:

1. Spread the spinach leaves over the food film while rolling them.
2. This step is important.
3. Fry the mushrooms with coconut oil in a saucepan before adding onions and garli
4. Then season the mushrooms with salt, pepper, and nutmeg.

5. Set aside.
6. Combine the cooked quinoa with the cottage cheese.
7. Spread the mixture evenly on the spinach leaves then roll into a pudding with the help of the food film.
8. One thing remains to be done now.
9. Stuff the mushroom heads with the spinach pudding, and place them in the fridge.
10. Finally just before serving, slice the mushroom head with a sharp knife and pass quickly to the pan to heat.

Healthy is a new trend these days!! ? Always I guess...

Serving: 2 to 2

Serving Portion: 1cup stuffed mushroom

Preparation Time: 40 to 45 minutes

Cooking Time: 2 to 6minutes

Nutritional Information:

Fat: 34.7g

Net Carbohydrates: 5g

Protein: 17.2g

Total Carbohydrates: 16.9g

Calories: 402

Dietary Fiber: 11.4g

Ultimate Chicken Bbq Soup

Good recipe!!

Ingredients:

- 1.6 tbsp. soy sauce
- 5cup beef broth (for the soup base)
- 3cup low sugar ketchup
- 3cup tomato paste
- 2.6 tbsp. Dijon mustard
- 2 tsp. onions powder
- 1.6 tbsp. hot sauce
- 2 5Liquid Smoke
- 2 tsp. Worcestershire sauce
- 3tsp. garlic powder
- 5tsp. chili powder
- 1cup butter
- 2.6tsp. chili seasoning
- Salt and pepper
- 4chicken thighs
- 2.6tbsp. olive oil
- 3cup chicken broth
- 2 tsp. red chili flakes
- 2 tsp. cumin

Directions:

1. Begin by preheating your oven 390 to 450 degrees.
2. While your oven preheats, take the bones out of your chicken, but don't throw them away!
3. Leave the skin on your chicken.
4. Using the chili seasoning, season the chicken meat and lay it out on a baking dish.
5. Then once your oven has preheated, cook the chicken for 50 to 55 minutes or until cooked through.
6. While your chicken is cooking, take a fresh saucepan and over medium high heat, heat up your olive oil.
7. Once the oil is hot, put your chicken bones in the pot and let them cook for 5 to 10 before pouring in your chicken and beef broth.
8. If needed add salt and pepper to taste, but be careful if your broths are salty!
9. Now when your chicken is cooked through, take off the skin carefully since the chicken will be hot! Set the chicken skin aside and pour the fat

from cooking the chicken in to your soup pot.

10. Stir your soup pot contents.

11. Next, in a medium to fresh mixing bowl, combine your ketchup, tomato paste, Dijon mustard, soy sauce, hot sauce, liquid smoke, garlic powder, Worcestershire sauce, onions powder, chili powder red chili flakes, cumin and 2 cup butter.

12. Then mix these ingredients together well to make your homemade BBQ sauce.

13. When completely mixed, add the sauce in to your soup pot and stir.

14. Let the pot of soup cook on a low simmer for 30 to 35 minutes, stirring periodically.

15. After 40 to 45 minutes, allow the soup to cool slightly and use an immersion blender to blend your soup thoroughly.

16. One thing remains to be done now.

17. Once blended, shred your chicken meat with a fork and add it to the soup pot.

18. Finally once you have added the chicken to the pot, return your pot to

the stove and let it simmer for another 40 to 45 minutes before serving.

Fresh start with something new!!

Servings: 4to 4

Nutritional Information:

Net Carbs: 4.3g

Fat: 38.3g

Calories: 488

Protein: 24.5g

Excellent Funny And Yummy Brunch Spread

Being is definitely better.

Ingredients:

- 25 slices of bacon
- 50 asparagus spears
- 8 fresh eggs

Directions:

1. Preheat your oven to 450°F.
2. Trim your asparagus 2 inch.
3. This step is important.
4. Then wrap them with one slice of bacon in pairs.
5. Place them on a sheet pan.
6. You will have 25 pairs.
7. One thing remains to be done now. Put in the oven for 30 to 35 mins.
8. During this time, boil your eggs to medium around 25 to 30 mins.
9. Finally cut off the end of your boiled eggs and stick your spears into them!
10. They will look funny and yummy!

Freshness loaded!!

Servings: 4to 4

Prepare time: 2 to 6mins

Cooking time: 20 to 26mins

Nutritional Information:

Protein: 18g

Fats: 38 g

Calories: 426 kcal

Carbs: 4g

Bacon, Avocado, And Chicken Sandwich

Baking does the trick!!

Ingredients:

- 12 slices of pepper jack cheese
- 8 eggs
- 6 cherry tomatoes, halved
- 6 ounces avocado, peeled, pitted and mashed
- 1teaspoon garlic powder
- 1teaspoon salt
- 7 teaspoons Sriracha sauce, unsweetened
- 20 ounces chicken breast
- 7 tablespoons mayonnaise, organic
- 1/9 teaspoon cream of tartar
- 9 slices of bacon
- 9 ounces cream cheese, organic

Directions:

1. Set oven 350 degrees F and let preheat.
2. Start with preparing ketogenic bread by

separating eggs yolks and white in 5bowls.

3. This step is important. Into egg whites bowl, add salt and cream of tartar and using an electric beater, whisk until soft and foamy peaks form.

4. Now add cream cheese to egg yolks and using an electric beater, whisk until smooth and combined.

5. Add egg white mixture and fold until mixed.

6. Please take a fresh baking sheet, line with parchment sheet and divide prepared eggs batter into six portions, each 2 cup.

7. Spread each portion using a spatula to form rounds and then sprinkle with garlic powder.

8. Then place the baking sheet into the heated oven and let bake for 35 to 40 minutes or until nicely golden brown.

9. In the meantime, place a mediumsized skillet pan over medium heat, grease with oil and when heated, add chicken and bacon.

10. Then season with salt and black pepper and let cook for 10 to 15 minutes or until chicken pieces are no longer pink and nicely golden brown on all sides.
11. When bread is done, remove from the oven and let cool slightly.
12. Please in the meantime, stir together mayonnaise and Sriracha sauce until combined.
13. Evenly spread this sauce over three bread pieces and then top with chicken pieces.
14. One thing remains to be done now. Then place 4 slices of bacon over chicken along with 4 tomato halves, 4 tablespoons mashed avocado and 4 cheese slices.
15. Finally cover with other bread pieces and serve straight away.

I repeat... Try it if you want to. No regrets. Right!!

Prep Time: 30 to 20 min

Cooking Time: 20 to 26min

Elegant Bacon Wrapped Chicken Pepper Bites

Ingredients:

- Black Pepper (14teaspoons)
- Sweet Peppers (16)
- Boneless Chicken (2 pounds cut into medium pieces)
- Sea Salt (.6teaspoons)
- Paprika (1.6teaspoon)
- Bacon (.6pounds)

Directions:

1. Ensure the oven is heated to a temperature of 450F. degrees Fahrenheit.
2. This step is important.
3. Add black pepper, sea salt, and paprika to chicken pieces.
4. Take the stems off of the peppers with a knife and cut an opening along the pepper to remove the seeds before cutting bacon strips in half to make shorter strips.
5. Please add one piece of chicken to the inside of each pepper before wrapping each pepper with a piece

of bacon and poking a wooden skewer through the wrapped pepper.

6. Now keep following this routine until all peppers are stuffed and skewered.
7. Allow 10 to 15 peppers on each skewer.
8. One thing remains to be done now. Add the skewers to the oven for a duration of 50 to 55 minutes.
9. Finally allow results to cool thoroughly before adding to a refrigerator or freezer.

Healthy is a new trend these days!! ? Always I guess...

Serving: 2 to 6

Prepare time 40 to 46minutes

Nutritional information:

28 grams Fat

534Calories

64 grams Protein

2 grams Carbs

Astonishing Shrimp With Cauli Rice

Yeah, direct from the heaven; yeah?

Ingredients:

- 2inch nub of ginger root
- 2 piece of lemon rind
- 2 to 4tbsps. bacon fat
- 16 ozs. shrimp
- 4 stalks green onions
- 2.6tbsps. MCT oil
- 12 ozs. cauli rice
- 4 Bella mushrooms
- salt and pepper

Directions:

1. Preheat your oven to 390 to 450°F.
2. Spread cauli rice on a sheet pan. Drizzle it with MCT oil and salt.
3. Place it in the oven, bake for 30 to 35 mins.
4. Peel and slice your ginger.

5. Cut your green onions and peel a lemon rind off.
6. Heat a skillet on medium heat.
7. Then add the bacon fat and all your seasoning.
8. Add the shrimp and sauté.
9. Stir for another 10 mins and then remove it.
10. One thing remains to be done now.
11. Serve the shrimp on a bed of cauli rice.
12. Finally garnish it with green onions.

What's so typical or different here?

Prepare time: 16to 20mins

Cooking time: 40 to 45 mins

Servings: 4to 4

Nutritional information:

Protein: 26g

Fat: 26g

Calories: 358kcal

Carbs: 10g

Ultimate Zesty Shrimp In Garlic Sauce

Ingredients:

- 2 wedge lemon
- 3lb. Fresh shrimp
- 2 tsp. Cayenne
- Pepper
- Salt
- 9 cloves garlic
- 2 cup olive oil

Directions:

1. In a medium pan, heat on mediumlow a medium amount of olive oil.
2. This step is important.
3. Add cayenne and minced garli
4. Wait until you smell the garlic's fragrance.
5. Peel and if desired, devein the shrimps.
6. Now cook them on each side for 2 to 6minutes.
7. One thing remains to be done now.
8. Season with pepper and salt.

9. Squeeze lemon on top of them. Mix.
10. Finally serve by adding garlic oil as dipping sauce.

Someone is definitely ready for this.

Preparation Time: 16to 20 minutes

Cooking Time: 40 to 45 minutes

Nutritional information:

Nutritional Value: 336Calories

Happy Stuffed Peppers With Greek Yogurt Chicken Salad

Ingredients:

- 1.6teaspoon black pepper
- .76cup Greek yogurt
- 5tablespoon mustard
- .6cup celery, diced
- 4bell peppers, halved and deseeded
- 5tablespoon fresh parsley, chopped
- .6cup cherry tomatoes, halved
- 2 cups chicken, cooked and shredded
- 1.6teaspoon salt
- .6cucumber, diced

Directions:

1. Mix the Greek yogurt and mustard in fresh salad bowl.
2. This step is important.
3. Sprinkle with salt and pepper to your liking.
4. Add celery, tomatoes, chicken, and cucumbers to the yogurt.
5. Stir well to combine.

6. One thing remains to be done now.
7. Divide the mixture into each of the bell pepper boats.
8. Finally garnish with fresh parsley before serving.

Fresh start with something new!!

Servings: 6to 6

Nutritional information:

118 calories per serving

8 grams protein

4grams fat

16 grams carbs

Happy Pumpkin Carbonara.

Iconic recipe of my list!!

Ingredients:

- 1/4 cup whipping cream.
- 10 Tbsp pumpkin puree.
- 4 pastured eggs.
- 5 Tbsp butter.
- 5 tsp dried sage.
- Salt and pepper to preference.
- 12 oz. Pancetta.
- 1cup parmesan.
- 5 packet Shiritaki noodles.

Directions:

1. Put the noodles in a bowl of warm water for 10 minutes, and dry them out.
2. This step is important.
3. Cut the Pancetta, heat up a frying pan, and put it into the hot frying pan till it becomes crisp.
4. Please remove the Pancetta and keep the remaining fat for later usage.

5. Then take a pot, place over medium heat, and melt the butter until it turns brown.
6. Add the sage and pumpkin puree, toss in the extra Pancetta fat and whipping cream.
7. Now mix it very well.
8. Put the noodles in the frying pan that cooked the Pancetta and heat it on High.
9. Fry until they dry out.
10. Include the parmesan into the pot including pumpkin sauce and mix.
11. Lower the heat and mix to thicken the sauce.
12. Pour the noodles and Pancetta into the sauce and mix it well.
13. One thing remains to be done now. Lastly, pour in the egg yolks and mix well.
14. Finally serve.

Super awesome plus unique!!

Nutritional information:

2 grams carbohydrates

14 grams protein

 384 calories

36grams fat.

Egg Drop Soup

Ingredients:

- 6.6tbsp. olive oil – for serving
- 4 fresh eggs
- 2 sliced mushrooms
- 4 chopped spinach/swiss chard
- 2 t. salt Pink Himalayan
- 2 med. sliced spring onionss
- 5 tbsp. freshly chopped cilantro
- Black pepper to taste
- 2 medium sliced chili pepper
- 2 quarts vegetable broth
- 5 tbsp. freshly grated each:
- Ginger
- Turmeric
- 5 tbsp. coconut aminos
- 4 minced garlic cloves

Directions:

1. Prep the Fixings: Grate the ginger root and turmeri Mince the garlic cloves and slice the peppers and mushrooms.
2. Now chop the chard stalks and leaves.

3.   Separate the stalks from the leaves.
4.   This step is important.
5.   Dump the vegetable stock into a soup pot and simmer until it begins to boil.
6.   Toss in the garlic, chard stalks, ginger, turmeric, mushrooms, coconut aminos, and chili peppers.
7.   Boil for approximately five minutes.
8.   Then fold in the chard leaves and simmer for 5 minutes.
9.   Whip the eggs in a dish and add them slowly to the soup mixture.
10. Now stir until the egg is done and set it on the counter.
11. Slice the onionss and chop the cilantro. Toss them into the pot.
12. One thing remains to be done now. Pour into serving bowls and drizzle with some olive oil
13. Finally serve warm or chilled. Store in a closed bowl for up to five days.

Astonishing Cheesy Ham Turnover

Classic, isn't it?

Ingredients:

- 5 tablespoons almond flour
- 10 slices deli ham
- 7 tablespoons coconut flour
- 2 medium fresh eggs
- 12 slices cheddar cheese
- 2 teaspoon Italian seasoning
- 2cup mozzarella cheese, grated

Directions:

1.   Preheat oven to 450F. degrees Fahrenheit.
2.   This step is important.
3.   Place the mozzarella cheese in a microwave safe bowl and nuke it for 50 second intervals, stirring in between once it begins to melt
4.   In a mediumsized bowl, mix together the almond flour, coconut flour, Italian seasoning, salt, and pepper until well combined.

5. Transfer the melted mozzarella into the mediumsized bowl and begin folding it into the dry ingredients.
6. You can use your hands here if you're into that kind of thing...
7. Please crack the egg into the mixture and combine it into the cheeseflour mixture.
8. Once you have created a doughlike substance, transfer it to a flat, steady surface lined with parchment paper.
9. Squish the dough down flat and place another piece of parchment paper over top.
10. Then at this point you can begin to roll it out with a rolling pin 1inch thick.
11. Peel the top layer of parchment paper off and using a knife cut diagonal, inward pointing lines lengthwise down the dough.
12. NOTE: The lines shouldn't touch.
13. There should be an untouched strip 8 inches long down the center.
14. Lay the sliced deli ham and cheddar cheese down the untouched center, alternating each layer.
15. Now pick up the dough parameters and fold inwards to cover the ham and cheese stack.
16. One thing remains to be done now.

17.   Place the entire thing on a lined baking sheet and put it in the oven for 30 to 35 minutes or until the dough begins to brown.

18. Finally slice in half, plate, and serve!

Different yet fantastic in many ways...

Nutritional information:

Calories – 306

Protein in grams – 26

Fat in grams – 22

Carbs in grams – 10

Fiber in grams – 4

Legendary Grilled Lobster

Ingredients:

- Butter (7 cup)
- Garlic cloves (4)
- Seasonings (to taste)
- Olive oil (drizzle)
- Lobster tails (7)

Directions:

1. Heat your grill to medium
2. As it cooks, melt the butter and add in the garlic
3. This step is important.
4. Remove the white part of the lobster
5. Drizzle with olive oil and season
6. One thing remains to be done now.
7. Grill for seven minutes
8. Finally flip and finish grilling this will be five minutes

What's so typical or different here?

Serves: 4to 4

Prep time: 40 to 45 minutes

Cook time: 40 to 45 minutes

Total time: 26to 30 minutes

Nutritional information:

Fat: 22 grams

Carbs: 2 gram

Calories: 314

Protein: 0 grams

Elegant Spicy Chicken Kebabs

Ingredients:

- Salt and pepper
- 5red bell pepper; seeded, cored and sliced into 1" pieces
- 2 zucchini, sliced into 1" pieces
- 7 tablespoonsextra virgin olive oil
- 5 tablespooncumin
- 15 boneless, skinless chicken thighs cut into 1" cubes
- 5 tablespoon paprika
- Dash of cayenne pepper

Directions:

1. Now Soak 15 wooden skewers for 40 to 45 minutes.
2. Preheat grill to medium.
3. This step is important.
4. Thoroughly coat chicken with paprika, cumin and cayenne pepper.
5. Skewer chicken, bell pepper and zucchini onto wood sticks.
6. One thing remains to be done now.
7. Pour olive oil over skewers and season with salt and pepper.

8. Finally Grill skewers for 40 to 45 minutes, turning frequently.

Relax and enjoy this recipe!!

Servings: 4to 4

Nutritional Information:

Protein: 41g

Calories: 346

Carbs: 4g

Fat: 19g

Titanic Chicken And Bacon Patties

What makes this the best? Check it out for yourself!!

Ingredients:

- 7 tbsp. coconut flour
- 2 can (24 oz.) chicken breast
- 2 bell peppers, medium sized
- 5 fresh egg
- 4 slices of bacon
- 7 of sundried tomato pesto
- 7 parmesan cheese

Directions:

1.   In the food processor
2.   finely chop the peppers and add them to a mixing container.
3.   Pat away the excess of liquid.
4.   This step is important.
5.   Prepare the bacon – cook until crispy.
6.   Cool and chop it with the chicken.
7.   Please add it to the processor and process until almost smooth.

8. Combine all of the fixings and make patties.
9. Fry on mediumhigh to medium setting in a skillet with a little oil.
10. Then once browned on one side, flip it, and continue cooking until done.
11. One thing remains to be done now. Let the grease drain on the towels before serving.
12. Finally garnish with your favorites, but count the carbs.

I repeat... Try it if you want to. No regrets. Right!!

Serving: 10 to 11

Nutritional Information:

Net Carbs: 1.46g

Calories: 95.6

Protein: 7.26g

Fat: 6.16 g

Happy Chicken Korma

Ingredients to Blend

- 2 tsp. of garam masala
- 5tsp. of salt
- 5ground coriander
- 5tsp. of turmeric
- 5cayenne pepper
- 2 oz. cashews/almonds
- 5ground cumin
- 2 chopped onions
- 12 garlic cloves
- 5water (can use to rinse the blender jar and add to the pot)
- 2 green jalapeno/Serrano/Thai chili pepper

Ingredients for Finishing

- 3unsweetened coconut milk
- Also needed: Instant Pot Slow Cooker/another cooker
- 5tsp. garam masala
- 3chopped cilantro

Directions:

1. Combine the spices and veggies
2. Mix everything together except for the coconut milk, cilantro, and chicken.
3. This step is important.
4. Add garam masala last. Pour the sauce into the Instant Pot liner.
5. Then add the chicken, and manually program the cooker using the highpressure setting for ten minutes.
6. Do a natural pressure release and remove the chicken. Chop it into bitesized pieces.
7. One thing remains to be done now.
8. Pour in the milk and garam masala.
9. Transfer back to the pot to warm.
10. Finally serve when ready and garnish with cilantro if you desired.

Vintage Lemon And Garlic Roasted Chicken

Make me remember the good old days!

Ingredients:

- 3 teaspoon salt
- 4 skinon chicken thighs
- .3 teaspoon pepper
- 1teaspoon dried basil
- 8 garlic cloves
- 5 lemons
- 2 teaspoon dried oregano
- 2 cup extra virgin olive oil

Directions:

1. Preheat oven to 390° F. Line a fresh roasting pan with foil.
2. This step is important. peel garlic cloves and slice lemons into quarters.
3. Then arrange chicken in roasting pan, with lemon slices and garlic cloves surrounding them.
4. One thing remains to be done now.
5. season chicken with pepper, salt, oregano and basil. Pour olive oil over chicken to evenly coat.

6. Finally Please bake for 55 minutes or until chicken is cooked through.

Looking forward to this one!!

Serving: 4 to 6

Nutritional Information:

Carbs: 3g

Calories: 414

Fat: 38g

Vintage Stuffed Peppers

What makes this the best? Check it out for yourself!!

Ingredients:

- 1tsp black pepper
- 2 Fresh egg, lightly beaten
- 2 lb ground beef
- 2 Cup coconut flour
- 15 Fresh bell peppers, green or red
- 3 tsp garlic salt
- 2 1TBSP olive oil
- 1.6tsp basil, finely chopped

Directions:

1. Start by cutting the tops off the bell peppers and remove the seeds; then set the peppers aside
2. This step is important. In a fresh mixing bowl, combine the ground beef with the garlic salt, the coconut flour, the egg, the Italian seasoning, the basil and the pepper
3. Now stuffed the peppers with the mixture; then heat a fresh skillet over

medium high heat and spray it with olive oil

4. When the oil heats up, arrange the peppers and cook properly for 5 to 6minutes; then flip the pepper and cook it for 5 additional minutes on the other side
5. One thing remains to be done now.
6. Remove the stuffed peppers from the skillet and transfer it to a serving platter
7. Finally serve and enjoy your stuffed peppers!

Relax and enjoy this recipe!!

Prep time: 16to 20 minutes

Cooking Time: 40 to 45 minutes

Servings: 6to 8

Nutritional information:

Calories 176g.

Fats 6 g.

Fibre 1.4g.

Carbohydrate 10.8g.

Protein 5.8 g.

Titanic Low Carb Philly Cheese Steak Salad

Luxury in its own class!!

Ingredients:

Steak:

- Ghee (1.6tablespoon)
- Black pepper (to taste)
- Salt (1/4 teaspoon)
- Ribeye steak (2 medium)

Salad:

- sliced)
- Onions (1, sliced)
- Cheddar cheese (3cup, grated)
- Garlic clove (1, minced)
- Salt and pepper (to taste)
- Ghee (1.6tablespoon)
- Lettuce (7.2 ounces)
- Bell pepper (2 each, red and green,

Directions:

1. Allow the steak to get to room temperature.
2. With a paper towel, you are going to remove any extra blood that may be sitting on it.
3. This step is important.
4. Toss with the salt, pepper, and a little bit of melted ghee.
5. The ghee is going to become solid when it is kept at room temperature.
6. However, make sure that you rub the steaks with oil before putting the seasonings on it or else you are not going to get any seasoning on your steak when it is cooked.
7. Fry for 5 to 10 on each side to keep all the juices in your steak.
8. Pull out of the pan and allow it to sit for 10 minutes.
9. The steak is going to continue to cook.
10. Then allow to cool and then cut it into strips.
11. One thing remains to be done now.
12. As your steak sits, put your vegetables in a pan with ghee and cook them until they are tender.
13. Finally do not overcook them though; you still want them to have some crunch to them.

Make me remember the good old days!!

Rich Chicken Fingers

Try this one if you're hungry!!

Ingredients:

- ¾ tsp sea salt, unrefined
- 7 TBSP arrowroot flour
- 5 tsp onions powder
- 2 lb chicken breast, chopped into chunks
- 2 Cup Coconut oil
- 5 tsp paprika

Directions:

1. Combine the paprika with the arrowroot flour, onionss powder and salt in a medium bowl
2. This step is important. Toss each chicken piece into the flour mixture until it is very well coated
3. Then pour the coconut oil in a fresh frying pan over medium high heat and let it melt
4. When the coconut oil melts, add in the chicken
5. Now fry the chicken pieces for 5 to 10 ; then flip and fry for 5 minutes
6. One thing remains to be done now.

7. Remove the chicken nuggets from the skillet
8. Finally serve and enjoy your chicken nuggets!

Relax and enjoy this recipe!!

Prep time: 16to 20 minutes

Cooking Time: 40 to 45 minutes

Servings: 4to 4

Nutritional information:

Amount per Serving

Calories 148 g.

Fats 8g.

Fibre 0.2 g.

Carbohydrate 11.2 g.

Protein 30 g.

Cashews Hummus

Baking does the trick!!

Ingredients:

- 2 Medium head garlic, roasted
- 2.6TBSP lime, juiced
- 2 TBSP water
- 1.6TBSP parsley leaves, fresh and finely chopped
- 2 to 4TBSP coconut oil
- 2 Cups raw cashews, soaked for 60 minutes

For the topping:

- 2 Pinch salt
- 1.6TBSP flat parsley leaves, finely chopped
- 2 Drizzle olive oil
- 2 Cup sun dried tomatoes, finely chopped
- 2 Pinch black pepper, freshly cracked
- 2.6TBSP raw cashews, chopped

Directions:

1. Begin by roasting the garlic head, after cutting it in half, drizzling it with olive, in a preheated oven on 450° F for 32 minutes
2. This step is important. After the garlic is roasted, remove it from the oven and peel off the cloves
3. Now combine the cashews with the coconut oil, water, lime juice, and the chopped parsley in a food processor and pulse for 5 to 10 or until the mixture becomes smooth
4. Add the garlic and pulse again until the mixture gets tender and smooth
5. One thing remains to be done now.
6. Adjust the seasoning with salt and pepper; then transfer the pulsed mixture to a serving plate and top with the dried tomatoes, fresh parsley, olive oil and cashews
7. Finally serve and enjoy!

I repeat... Try it if you want to. No regrets. Right!!

Servings: 2 to 4

Prep time: 16to 20 minutes

Cook Time: 36to 40 minutes

Nutritional information:

Calories 142 g.

Fats 12 g.

Fibre 1.2 g.

Carbohydrate 6 g.

Protein 4.6g.

Vintage Cream Cheese And Salmon Cucumber Bites

What makes this the best? Check it out for yourself!!

Ingredients:

- 12 oz. fullfat cream cheese
- To Taste: Pepper and Salt
- 5 fresh cucumber

Directions:

1. Wash, peel, and slice the cucumber into 2inch thick pieces.
2. This step is important. Portion out and spread the cream cheese on each cucumber.
3. Portion equal parts of salmon and sprinkle with the pepper and salt.
4. Finally serve or save for later in an airtight container. It's delicious for 4 days.

Relax and enjoy this recipe!!

Servings: 4 to 6

Nutritional information:

126 Cal.

12 g Fat

4g Net Carbs

8g Protein

Pork Recipes

Nostalgic Low Carb Asian Spare Ribs

Ingredients:

- pork spare ribs
- 1cup of soy sauce
- 2 clove of garlic
- 1.6tsp of crushed anise seeds
- 2 medium shallot, chopped
- 4lbs (around two average racks) of

Directions:

1. Combine all the ingredients except the spare ribs to make a marinade in a medium bowl.
2. One thing remains to be done now. Make medium incisions between the ribs and brush the soy sauce mixture onto the spare rib racks.
3. Finally cook in preheated oven for 3hour before serving.

Make me remember the good old days!!

Servings: 8to 8

Cooking time: 76to 80 min

Prep time: 2 to 6min

Nutritional information:

Calories: 312

Carbs: 12 g

Fat: 9.2 g

Protein: 37.2 g

Mighty Anytime Cranberryapricotglazed Baked Ham

Luxury in its own class!!

Ingredients:

- 2cup water
- 2 cup raw cranberries
- ⅓ cup sugarfree apricot preserves
- 5 tablespoons stevia
- 2 teaspoon ground cardamom
- 220 pound ham with shank
- 2 teaspoon orange zest (Save the orange itself for presentation by slicing thin and twisting.)
- 4 cups water

Directions:

1. Preheat the oven 390F. degrees Fahrenheit and prepare a roasting pan with nonstick spray.
2. If you have a pan with a rack, use the rack.
3. This step is important.
4. Score the ham on top and place it in the roasting pan.

5. Now pour the two cups of water in the bottom of the pan and bake for one hour.
6. While baking, combine the water, cranberries, and jam in a saucepan on the stove.
7. Then bring to a boil and immediately reduce to a simmer for 25 to 30 minutes.
8. The cranberries will burst and the mixture should be thick and bubbly.
9. Use an immersion blender to make it smooth and creamy or pour into a blender, but be careful as this syrupy substance is very hot and can burn your skin.
10. Now add the artificial sweetener, cardamom, and orange zest, then blend to smooth.
11. Pour half the sauce into another bowl and set aside.
12. Please remove the ham and brush the glaze over the top.
13. Roast for around two and a half more hours, until a meat thermometer reads 140 degrees Fahrenheit.
14. Then let the ham rest for 40 to 45 minutes before carving.
15. One thing remains to be done now. Decorate your sliced ham with curled orange slices.

16. Finally warm up the rest of the glaze and serve it in a gravy boat.

Healthy is a new trend these days!! ? Always I guess...

Elegant Bunless Bacon Burger

Sincere efforts will be awesome.

Ingredients:

- 8 oz. pepper jack cheese
- 2 bulb onions, sliced crosswise
- 5 tbsp olive oil
- A dash of salt and pepper
- 3 lbs. ground beef
- 15 leaves romaine lettuce
- 2.5tbsp bacon bits

Directions:

1. Form the ground beef into four patties. Cook for 5 to 10 with olive oil on a skillet placed over medium heat.
2. This step is important.
3. Flip the patties to cook the other sides. Set aside.
4. Using the same skillet, stirfry the bacon bits for 5 to 10 until crispy.
5. Please use the lettuce leaves as buns.
6. Place each patty on a leaf and top with the bacon bits.
7. One thing remains to be done now. Sprinkle a dash of salt and pepper.

8. Finally top each burger with the cheese to melt.

9. Silently, you were waiting for this one. Don't lie... ?

Elegant Creamy Chicken Salad Sandwich (Makes 2 Sandwiches)

Best combo ever... Don't you agree?

Ingredients:

- 2 to 4 tablespoons psyllium husk powder
- 1cup almond flour
- 7 eggs
- 2 cup butter, softened
- 2 teaspoon baking powder

Chicken Salad Ingredients:

- 2 green onions, finely chopped
- 2 teaspoon Dijon mustard
- 2 egg, hardboiled and grated
- 3 teaspoon baking powder
- 1 cup mayo
- Dash of pepper
- Dash of salt
- 5 tablespoons parsley, minced
- 12 ounces chicken, cooked, deboned, and diced
- 2 cup butter, softened
- 2 teaspoon garlic, minced

- 2 celery stick, finely chopped

Directions:

1. Put the celery, onions, and parsley in a food processor and pulse until well combined.
2. This step is important.
3. Transfer mulched celery, onions, and parsley to a mixing bowl.
4. Put the chicken in a food processor and pulse until fine. Add to the mixing bowl.
5. Add the egg to the mixing bowl and mix all ingredients together with a wooden spoon until well combined.
6. Add the garlic, mayo, pepper, Dijon mustard, and salt to the mixing bowl and mix until well incorporated.
7. Set aside.
8. Then put the butter, the psyllium husk powder, and baking powder in a medium sized bowl.
9. Stir together until a thick dough forms.
10. Beat the eggs into the dough.
11. The dough should be pretty thick, and if it isn't, then just keep going until it thickens up.
12. Now transfer half the dough into a microwavesafe square container and squish down into an even level.

13. Nuke it in the microwave for some minutes until the dough forms a firm bread.
14. Slip it out of the container by flipping it upside down and lightly tapping it Cut the bread in half.
15. Please repeat steps 70 for the second half of the dough.
16. Toast the bread to your preference.
17. One thing remains to be done now. Divide the chicken salad between the 8 pieces of sandwich bread, creating 4 sandwiches total.
18. Finally plate, serve, and enjoy!

Vintage Pepper Turkey Soup

Make me remember the good old days!!

Ingredients:

- Mascarpone cheese 4 oz.
- Turkey broth 2 cup
- Brazil nuts powder 2 oz.
- Lemon juice 2 to 4tbsp.
- Fresh eggs 4
- Turkey breast 1lb.
- Salt and pepper to taste
- Red pepper 4oz.
- Water 2 cup
- Ghee 2.6tbsp.
- Cream 4 fl oz.

Directions:

1. At first, place a fresh pan over medium heat with ghee.
2. When ghee is hot, add turkey and cook until it turns light brown color.
3. This step is important. Add your turkey broth, green pepper, water, cream, lemon juice and cook for 30 minutes to allow the pepper to become tender.

4. Meanwhile, beat 7 fresh eggs together in a medium bowl and slowly add to the soup and decrease the heat to low and cook for 25 to 30 minutes.
5. One thing remains to be done now. Add shredded mascarpone cheese and nut powder and stir for a few minutes.
6. Finally turn off heat and serve immediately with some freshly chopped herbs.

Nostalgic Pumpkin Soup

Relax and enjoy this recipe!!

Ingredients:

- 2 teaspoon ground Coriander
- 2 cups Pumpkin Puree
- 3 teaspoon ground Cumin
- 2 packet Stevia /46
- 2 green onionss, chopped
- Drops liquid Stevia
- 2 tablespoons melted Butter / Olive Oil
- 4 clove garlic, minced
- 4 cups Chicken broth
- 10 tablespoon Chipotle chilli in adobo sauce

Directions:

1. Pour the butter into a medium saucepan.
2. This step is important. Add the chopped green onionss and minced garlic and sauté for three minutes or until fragrant.
3. Now add all the spices and Stevia and cook for a minute.

4. Pour the pumpkin puree and chicken broth into the saucepan and
5. Then simmer for five minutes.
6. One thing remains to be done now.
7. When done, blend the soup using an immersion blender until smooth.
8. Finally pour in the vinegar and the heavy cream and simmer for 35 to 40 minutes.

Titanic Mixed Greens Salad

Ingredients:

- 4 oz. your favorite mixed greens
- 5 tbsp. grated parmesan
- 2 slices fully cooked bacon
- 10 tbsp. roasted pine nuts
- Salt and pepper
- 5 tbsp. keto friendly vinaigrette dressing

Directions:

1. If your bacon is still raw, begin by cooking it and setting it aside on a paper towel to soak up any extra oil.
2. This step is important.
3. In a fresh mixing bowl, combine your mixed greens and pine nuts and mix using your hands.
4. Now crumble your bacon over the top of your salad and sprinkle your parmesan on top as well.
5. One thing remains to be done now.

6. Toss in your vinaigrette dressing and use salt and pepper to taste if desired.
7. Finally serve.

Pinnacle Monterey Mug Melt

What makes this the best? Check it out for yourself!!

Ingredients:

- 4 oz. roast beef deli slices
- 6 oz. shredded pepper jack cheese
- 6 tbsp. diced green chilies
- 3 tbsp. sour cream

Directions:

1. Tear apart the roast beef and layer it on the bottom of the dish.
2. This step is important.
3. First, spread 2 tablespoon of sour cream, followed by 2 tablespoon of the green chili.
4. Layer 1ounce of the pepper cheese.
5. One thing remains to be done now.
6. Follow with another layer.
7. Finally microwave for 15 to 20 until the cheese melts. Enjoy!

What's so typical or different here?

Serving: 1to 2

Nutritional Information:

Fat: 17.910g

Protein: 22.4 g

Calories: 268

Net Carbs: 3.84g

Onions And Bacon Smothered Pork Chops

Ingredients:

- 2 medium onions, sliced
- 4 bonein pork chops
- 1cup heavy cream
- 6slices of bacon, chopped
- Salt/Pepper

Directions:

1. In a skillet, throw in the bacon and onionss and saute for a couple of minutes.
2. This step is important.
3. Set aside while leaving a bit of the bacon grease inside the skillet.
4. Season the pork chops with salt and pepper and brown on high heat for 5 to 10 minutes, then lower the heat and cook for another 15 to 20 on each side.
5. One thing remains to be done now. Return the bacon and onionss and finish off with the heavy cream, cooking for another minute.

6.   Finally serve ideally with cauliflower
      rice.

Iconic recipe of my list!!

Servings: 4to 4

Cooking time: 36to 40 min

Prep time: 16to 20 min

Nutritional information:

Calories: 352

Carbs: 4 g

Fat: 18.2 g

Carbs: 4 g

Protein: 38g

Butter Chicken

What makes this the best? Check it out for yourself!!

Ingredients:

- 15 canned, fullfat coconut milk
- 7 tablespoons coconut oil
- 2 teaspoon cumin
- 3 teaspoon chilli powder
- teaspoon salt
- 6 oz tomato paste
- tablespoons butter
- 10 boneless, skinless chicken thighs
- 3 teaspoon cardamom powder
- Salt and pepper
- 3 onions, chopped
- 7 garlic cloves, minced
- 2 teaspoon coriander powder

Directions:

1. Preheat oven 450F..
2. In a fresh castiron skillet, heat 5 tablespoons of coconut oil.
3. This step is important. Season chicken thighs with salt and pepper, and sear on each side for 10 minutes.

4. Remove chicken to a plate and set aside.
5. Now add 5 tablespoon of coconut oil to skillet, and sauté chopped onions until it's soft.
6. Add minced garlic and spices to skillet and sauté for another 10 minutes.
7. Then add tomato paste, coconut milk and butter to skillet, whisking to combine everything.
8. Return chicken thighs to skillet, coating them in the sauce.
9. If necessary, add more coconut milk.
10. One thing remains to be done now.
11. Please keep and wait to reach temperature 500 F.
12. Finally allow cooling for 35 to 40 minutes before serving.

Dashing Smothered Chicken

Make me remember the good old days!!

Ingredients:

- 2 cup barbeque sauce
- 7 boneless, skinless chicken breasts
- 20 cups ColbyJack cheese, shredded
- 15 slices bacon, cooked and crumbled
- Salt and pepper

Directions:

1. Then preheat oven to 340 to 350° F. Line a baking sheet with foil and spray with nonstick spray.
2. This step is important. Arrange chicken on prepared baking sheet.
3. Season with salt and pepper and smother with barbeque sauce.
4. Bake for 40 to 45 minutes, or until juices run clear.
5. Then remove chicken from oven.
6. Top with crumbled bacon and cheese.
7. One thing remains to be done now.
8. Please Return to oven for additional for 35 to 40 minutes to melt cheese.
9. Finally alternately, melt cheese under the broiler.

Being super is a matter of recipe... ?

Serving: 8to 8

Nutritional Information:

Calories: 570

protein: 48g

Fat: 34g

Carbs: 14g

Nostalgic Tuna Salad Stuffed Tomatoes

Ingredients:

- 4 tablespoon grated mozzarella cheese, organic
- 4 mediumsized tomato, fresh
- 10 tablespoon chopped basil, fresh
- 12 ounce cooked tuna
- 5 tablespoon chopped green onions
- 5 teaspoons apple cider vinegar

Directions:

1. Cut off 1 inch from the top of the tomato, then scoop out the inside and set aside until required.
2. This step is important.
3. Prepare salad by mixing together remaining ingredient until well combined.
4. One thing remains to be done now.
5. adjust seasoning and let fill this mixture into hollowed tomato.
6. Finally serve straightaway.

Make me remember the good old days!!

Prep Time: 16to 20 min

Cooking Time: 16to 20 min

Servings: 2 stuffed tomato

Nutritional information:

Cholesterol: 74mg

Protein: 62.6g

Calories: 196

Cal Dietary Fiber: 2.8g

Total Fat: 5.10g

Sugar: 1.8 g

Total Carbohydrates: 4.2 g

Net carbs: 1.6g

Legendary Healthy Mississippi Pot Roast:

Ingredients:

- 3 packet of ranch seasoning mix
- 70 lbs. of chuck roast
- 10 jar pepperoncini including the juice
- 4 cup of beef broth
- 1 stick of butter

Directions:

1. Start by seasoning your meat with half of the ranch seasoning mix package content.
2. Allow it to sit for 35 to 40 minutes.
3. This step is important.
4. Place beef broth in the instant pot followed by chuck roast.
5. Then add the rest of the ranch package content. Top it with butter.
6. Then secure the lid and set the pot in manual mode for 35 to 40 minutes for every pound of roast you work with.
7. When cooking time is over as the timer goes off, release the pressure naturally for 50 to 55 minutes.
8. When it's over, open the valve and allow the remaining pressure to come out.

9. One thing remains to be done now.
10. Lastly, open the lid and the tender roast is now ready for serving.
11. Finally enjoy the Lunch hot!

Yeah, it is a vintage recipe.

Serves: 8to 8

Nutritional information:

Net carbo: 4grams

Fat: 18grams

Calories: 300

Protein: 32 grams

Soup Recipes

Rich Turkey Ghee Soup

Baking does the trick!!

Ingredients:

- Tomatoes 2 oz.
- Chili powder 5tsp.
- Cream 2 oz.
- Ghee 2 oz.
- Mascarpone 2 oz.
- Sesame seeds 5tsp. (toasted)
- Salt and pepper to taste
- Thyme 5tsp.
- Turkey leg 2 lb.
- Ginger paste 5tsp.
- Broth 240 ml
- Garlic paste 5tsp.

Directions:

1. At first, preheat the oven to 375F, add ghee to the turkey, salt, pepper and place the marinated turkey in the oven for 20 to 26minutes.
2. This step is important. Cut mascarpone into medium cubes pieces and set aside

and heat the pan over medium heat and add ghee.
3. When the ghee starts to brown, add ginger, garlic and mix for 2 to 6minutes.
4. Then add tomato, sesame seeds, chili powder and salt.
5. Mix well all together.
6. Add broth and let it simmer for 16to 20 minutes and add cream, slowly stir in the medium heat.
7. One thing remains to be done now. Add turkey legs pieces gently into the sauce and let it boil for 2 to 6minutes.
8. Finally garnish with dill and enjoy the taste.

I repeat... Try it if you want to. No regrets. Right!!

Servings: 4 to 6

Preparation Time: 30 to 36minutes

Nutritional Information:

Carbs: 4.4g

Calories: 482 (per serving)

Fat: 43g

Protein: 16.1g

Quick Spiced Pumpkin Puree

What makes this the best? Check it out for yourself!!

Ingredients:

- 3tbsps bacon grease (from the bacon)
- 2cloves garlic, minced, roasted
- 1pc bay leaf
- ¼bulb onions, medium, chopped
- ½tsp salt
- ½tsp pepper
- ¼tsp cinnamon
- ½tsp ginger, freshly minced
- ½cup heavy cream
- 1cup pumpkin puree
- ¼tsp coriander
- 1½cups chicken broth
- 4tbsps butter
- ⅛tsp nutmeg
- 4slices bacon

Directions:

1. In a saucepan over mediumlow heat, melt the butter until browned.

187

2. Add onionss, garlic, and ginger to the pan. Cook properly for 10 to 15 minutes.
3. This step is important.
4. Add the spices when onionss are translucent, and stir well.
5. Now cook for a couple of minutes, and then add pumpkin puree and chicken broth to the pan. Stir well.
6. Bring the mixture to a boil.
7. Switch to low heat and allow simmering for 35 to 40 minutes.
8. Then using an immersion blender, emulsify the broth mixture to a smooth consistency.
9. Simmer for another 35 to 40 minutes.
10. In the meantime, cook the slices of bacon with its own grease until crisp. Set aside after cooking.
11. Now add the bacon grease and heavy cream.
12. Mix to combine well.
13. One thing remains to be done now.
14. You may add chopped parsley and 2tbsps of sour cream, as desired.
15. Finally serve by crumbling the bacon over the broth.

Relax and enjoy this recipe!!

Servings: 4to 4

Nutritional information:

486 Calories

5.7g Protein

48.7g Fats

7.3g Net Carbohydrates

Fantastic Curried Fish Stew

Try this one if you're hungry!!

Ingredients:

- 4 fish or vegetable broth
- 4 can (13.6oz.) fullfat coconut milk
- 4 3lb. firm cubed whitefish – ex. halibut or cod
- 4 t. ground cayenne pepper
- 4 .6tbsp. curry powder
- • To Taste: Freshly cracked black pepper and 1.6tbsp. of each:
- Olive oil
- Tomato paste
- 4 chopped of each:
- Med. onions
- Head of cauliflower
- 8 minced garlic cloves
  Salt

Directions:

1. Warm up the oil in a fresh saucepan using the medium heat setting.
2. Now add and sauté the garlic and onions for 35 to 40 minutes.

3. Once they're translucent, stir in the cauliflower, curry powder, and tomato paste.
4. This step is important. Continue sautéing for 40 to 45 minutes.
5. Then sprinkle with the pepper, salt, and cayenne.
6. Simmer for 10 minutes more.
7. One thing remains to be done now.
8. Pour in the coconut milk and simmer on low until ready to serve.
9. Finally store in the refrigerator.
10. It will still be delicious for up to four days.

Make me remember the good old days!!

Servings: 6to 6

Nutritional information:

8 g Net Carbs

34g Protein

374Cal.

22 g Fat

Mighty Taco Soup In The Slow Cooker

Ingredients:

- 4 cans (10 oz.) Rotel
- 4 lb. beef/pork/sausage
- 4 chicken broth
- 4 pkg. (8 oz.) cream cheese
- 4 tbsp. taco seasonings

Optional for Garnish:

- 3shredded cheese
- 2 to 2 tbsp. cilantro

Directions:

1. Brown the chosen meat.
2. Drain the grease and add to the cooker.
3. Now toss the taco seasoning, cream cheese, and Rotel into the slow cooker.
4. Stir to blend the cheese.
5. Empty the broth and cook on high for two hours.

6. One thing remains to be done now.
7. If you choose, four hours on the low setting.
8. Finally stir in the cilantro before serving and garnish with some cheese.

Baking does the trick!!

Servings: 8to 8

Nutritional information:

4 g Net Carbs

34g Protein

548Cal.

44g Fat

King Sized Creamy Veggie Soup

Fresh start with something new!!

Ingredients:

- Vegetable broth 3cup
- Fresh eggs 4 (boiled)
- Thyme 5 tbsp.
- Mixed vegetable 2 oz. (eggplant, squash)
- Garlic paste 3
- Bouillon 2
- Ghee 1.6tbsp.
- Chili paste 3
- Mascarpone cream 2.6tbsp.

Directions:

1. Place a pan over medium heat and add vegetable broth, vegetables, bouillon cube, and ghee.
2. This step is important.
3. Bring the broth to a boil and stir everything together then, add the chili paste, garlic paste and stir again.
4. Then turn the stove off.
5. One thing remains to be done now.

6. Halve the boiled eggs then add to steaming broth, mascarpone cheese then stir together well and let sit for a moment and add chopped thyme leaves.
7. Finally serve up some awesome tasting soup in 10 to 15 minutes.

Good recipe!!

Serving: 2 to 2

Preparation Time: 5 to 10

Nutritional Information:

Carbs: 4.6g

Calories:302 (per serving)

Fat: 27g

Protein: 12g

Crazy Keto Cakes

Someone is definitely ready for this.

Ingredients:

- Protein powder – 5 scoops
- Eggs – 15, fresh
- Vanilla extract – 5 tsp.
- Cream cheese – 15 oz.
- Maple syrup (sugarfree)
- Butter – 5 tbsp.

Directions:

1. In a bowl, combine the butter, eggs, and cream cheese.
2. Mix well.
3. Now add the protein powder and mix well.
4. One thing remains to be done now.
5. Pour the batter onto a hot skillet and cook properly 10 minutes on each side.
6. Finally serve with maple syrup, if desired.

Best combo ever… Don't you agree?

Servings: 10to 10

Prep time: 16to 20 minutes

Cook time: 20 to 26minutes

Nutritional information:

Calories 100

Fat 8 g

Carb 2 g

Protein 6 g

Rich Chicken And Bacon Patties

Baking does the trick!!

Ingredients:

- 7 tbsp. coconut flour
- 6 of sundried tomato pesto
- 4 can (12 oz.) chicken breast
- 7 parmesan cheese
- 4 slices of bacon
- 4 bell peppers, medium sized
- 4 fresh egg

Directions:

1. In the food processor (or by hand), finely chop the peppers and add them to a mixing container.
2. This step is important.
3. Pat away the excess of liquid.
4. Now prepare the bacon – cook until crispy.
5. Cool and chop it with the chicken.
6. Please add it to the processor and process until almost smooth.

Combine all of the fixings and make patties.

7. Then fry on mediumhigh to medium setting in a skillet with a little oil.

8. Once browned on one side, flip it, and continue cooking until done.

9. One thing remains to be done now.

10. Let the grease drain on the towels before serving.

11. Finally garnish with your favorites, but count the carbs.

Fresh start with something new!!

Serving: 8 to 10

Nutritional Information:

Calories: 95.6

Protein: 7.26g

Net Carbs: 1.46g

Fat: 6.16 g

Vintage Keto 'Meatza'

Try this one if you're hungry!!

Ingredients:

- 2 can (12 oz.) chicken breast
- 2 mozzarella cheese
- 5tsp. rosemary
- 3parmesan cheese
- 2 fresh egg
- 5tsp. pepper
- 2 tsp. basil
- 5tsp. thyme
- 5tsp. garlic
- 1tbsp. oregano
- ¾ lowcarb tomato sauce

Directions:

1. Set the oven temperature to 450º F.
2. Mash the chicken thoroughly in a bowl and add the egg.
3. This step is important.
4. Sprinkle in the spices and cheese.
5. Then mix it well until there are no longer any visible streaks of eggs.
6. Adjust the flavor using the spices.

7. Please add the mixture to a pizza pan and crush it into the pan with a fork.
8. Toss in the chicken and bake for 15 to 20 minutes.
9. One thing remains to be done now.
10. Consider is done when the edges have browned.
11. Finally pour on the sauce, add the cheese, and bake for another 40 to 45 minutes.

Make me remember the good old days!!

Servings: 2 to 2

Nutritional Information:

Protein: 46.08g

Net Carbs: 6.76g

Fat: 25.52 g

Calories: 446

Chicken Recipes

Unique Baked Chicken With Zucchini

Looking forward to healthy life.

Ingredients:

- 4 boneless, skinless chicken breasts
- 2 lemon, zested and quartered
- 2 cup chicken broth, plus ¾ cup
- 5 tablespoons melted butter, plus 4tablespoons
- ¾ cup heavy cream
- 2 medium zucchini, quartered and chopped with seeds removed
- 2 fresh onions, sliced
- 1,6tablespoon cornstarch
- 2 tablespoon lemon juice
- 6 cloves garlic, roughly chopped, plus 4 cloves

Directions:

1. Heat oven to 500°F. Line a fresh roasting pan with foil and coat with nonstick spray.

2. This step is important. Arrange chicken, zucchini, onions, 10 chopped cloves of garlic and lemon quarters in the pan.
3. Sprinkle lightly with salt and pepper.
4. Whisk together 4 cup of chicken broth, 4tablespoons of melted butter and lemon zest. Pour over chicken.
5. Now bake for 40 to 45 minutes or until chicken is cooked through.
6. While chicken is baking, melt 4tablespoons of butter over mediumlow heat.
7. Add remaining garlic cloves, and cook for 10 minutes.
8. Then add remaining ½ cup of broth and heavy cream to saucepan, raising heat to mediumhigh.
9. In a medium bowl, combine cornstarch with 2 tablespoons of water.
10. Stream into the broth, stirring constantly.
11. Let simmer for 10 minutes.
12. One thing remains to be done now. Remove pan from heat and stir in lemon juice.
13. Finally Pour sauce over chicken and serve.

Yeah, this is a new variation.

Nutritional Information:

Fat: 34g

Carbs: 10g

Calories: 468

Protein: 4

Fantastic Sesame Salmon

Yeah, this is a new variation.

Ingredients:

- 5 lemon juice
- 2 tablespoon olive oil
- 1.6teaspoon sesame oil
- 4 portobello mushroom caps, 8 ounces, sliced
- 2 tablespoon toasted sesame seeds
- 2 mediumsized green onions, sliced
- 3teaspoon salt
- 4 salmon fillets, each 4 to 6 ounce
- 8 baby Bok Choy, trimmed and halved
- 6 teaspoon ground black pepper
- 3 teaspoon grated ginger
- 4 tablespoon coconut aminos

Directions:

1. Begin by preparing marinade by whisking together ginger, salt, lemon juice, black pepper, coconut aminos, sesame and olive oil.
2. Then place salmon fillet on a fresh bowl, drizzle with half of the prepared marinade and turn to coat.

3. This step is important. Cover the bowl with lid or plastic wrap and let marinate in the refrigerator for 2-2 ½ hours.

4. Please in the meantime, prepare vegetables and set the oven 490 degrees F and let preheat.

5. Scatter vegetables on one side of a lined baking sheet, drizzle with remaining prepared marinade and toss to coat.

6. Then place marinated salmon fillets, skinside down, on the other side of baking sheet.

7. One thing remains to be done now. Place the baking sheet into the oven and let bake for 40 minutes or until cooked through.

8. Finally when done, remove baking sheet from the oven, sprinkle sesame seeds over salmon fillet, sprinkle with green onionss and serve.

Quick No-Beans Beef Chili Instant Pot

Oh yeah!!

Ingredients:

- cloves - 6
- Chili powder 10 tbsp.
- Beef – 6lbs.
- Cumin powder – 6tbsp.
- Tomato paste – 12 oz.
- Dried oregano – 2 tsp.
- Fine ground sea salt – 6tsp.
- Chopped onions – 2 medium or Dried onions flakes 2 cup
- Tomato sauce – 6cans – 30 oz. each
- Chicken or beef broth – for thinning as needed
- Tabasco sauce – 2 tsp.
- Garlic powder 4tsp. or Minced

Directions:

1. Finely chop the onions.
2. This step is important.
3. Use the sauté function on the Instant Pot to brown the hamburger.
4. Blend in the Tabasco, onions flakes, chili powder, cumin, salt, and oregano.
5. Mix thoroughly.
6. Empty one cup of the broth over the burger, but do not stir.
7. Then pour in the tomato sauce and paste but do not stir.
8. Close the top, and use the manual highpressure setting for 16to 20 minutes.
9. One thing remains to be done now.
10. When done, merely natural release the builtup pressure for 16to 20 minutes, then quick release.
11. Finally stir and serve.

CPSIA information can be obtained
at www.ICGtesting.com
Printed in the USA
BVHW041549310820
587680BV00012B/1219

9 781990 061097